FATHER'S PATERNAL GRANDFATHER'S FULL NAME

FATHER'S PATERNAL GRANDMOTHER'S FULL NAME

DATE OF MARRIAGE PLACE OF MARRIAGE

CHILDREN

FATHER'S GREAT-GRANDFATHER'S FULL NAME

FATHER'S GREAT-GRANDMOTHER'S FULL NAME

FATHER'S GREAT-GRANDFATHER'S FULL NAME

FATHER'S GREAT-GRANDMOTHER'S FULL NAME

FATHER'S MATERNAL GRANDFATHER'S FULL NAME

FATHER'S MATERNAL GRANDMOTHER'S FULL NAME

DATE OF MARRIAGE PLACE OF MARRIAGE

CHILDREN

FATHER'S GREAT-GRANDFATHER'S FULL NAME

FATHER'S GREAT-GRANDMOTHER'S FULL NAME

FATHER'S GREAT-GRANDFATHER'S FULL NAME

FATHER'S GREAT-GRANDMOTHER'S FULL NAME

MOTHER'S PATERNAL GRANDFATHER'S FULL NAME

MOTHER'S PATERNAL GRANDMOTHER'S FULL NAME

DATE OF MARRIAGE PLACE OF MARRIAGE

CHILDREN

MOTHER'S GREAT-GRANDFATHER'S FULL NAME

MOTHER'S GREAT-GRANDMOTHER'S FULL NAME

MOTHER'S GREAT-GRANDFATHER'S FULL NAME

MOTHER'S GREAT-GRANDMOTHER'S FULL NAME

MOTHER'S MATERNAL GRANDFATHER'S FULL NAME

MOTHER'S MATERNAL GRANDMOTHER'S FULL NAME

DATE OF MARRIAGE PLACE OF MARRIAGE

CHILDREN

MOTHER'S GREAT-GRANDFATHER'S FULL NAME

MOTHER'S GREAT-GRANDMOTHER'S FULL NAME

MOTHER'S GREAT-GRANDFATHER'S FULL NAME

MOTHER'S GREAT-GRANDMOTHER'S FULL NAME

PLEASE TURN TO THE INSIDE BACK PAGE TO COMPLETE YOUR FAMILY TREE →

Our
Family
HISTORY

THIS CERTIFIES THAT

AND

WERE UNITED IN HOLY MATRIMONY

PLACE OF CEREMONY ______________________

TOWN/CITY/COUNTY ______________________

MONTH __________ DAY __________ YEAR __________

MARRIED BY ______________________

First Published in 1998
by Montage Editions Limited
21 Catherine Street, Covent Garden, London WC2B 5JS

Reprinted 2000, 2001, 2003

ISBN 1-902403-03-7

Designed by Paul Vater at Sugar Free, London
Picture Research by The Jan Croot Collection, Brighton, UK
Printed and bound in China

HISTORY

Our Family Tree

Research

The Family

Family Profiles

Special Occasions

Family Stories

Family Friends

Family Belongings

FAMILY NOTES

FAMILY NOTES

OUR FAMILY HISTORY

Introduction

A family history, complete with a full family tree, is a true heirloom. This volume opens with a family tree, in which to record the names and dates of direct family members. There is then space to write detailed profiles of your ancestors, your parents, your siblings, and your extended family. There are sections for family tales, family belongings, family homes, and all the other things that make your family special. You can include family photographs throughout, and the final part of the volume gives you space to trace your family's past and present in pictures. In completing this book, you are creating a rich and detailed tapestry of your family history, which will be an object of great value to future generations.

Compiling this unique history will enrich the family's knowledge of its roots and its heritage. By your efforts, you can gather vital information that might otherwise become lost in the mists of time. The next generation will have a picture of their ancestry, and a sense of their past.

Compiling a family history is like completing a huge jigsaw–initially you may have no idea where each piece of information fits in, but, as time passes, the facts interlock to form a complete picture. You may find that to start with it is difficult to establish the facts about your family. In an age when people are mobile, and families may be spread all over a country, or even around the world, it can be a challenge to trace all the family members. But do not be discouraged: proceed step by step, and remember that the more you find out, the easier the task becomes.

To gather information about your roots is to preserve an important piece of history.

Keep the following in mind when gathering information:

- Enlist the help of as many family members as possible, and keep them up to date with your progress–the more detectives there are, the more will be discovered!

- Talk to older members of the family–their memories will be very important in your search.

- Use old family photographs, documents, and portraits to stimulate people's memory.

- Remember that no detail, however trivial, is unimportant–try to find out not just birth dates, but also professions, hobbies, and idiosyncrasies, so you have a fuller picture of your forebears.

- Local archives can be a great source of information if your family has been based in a particular area over a number of generations.

Most of all, enjoy the challenge. Remember, this is not just a book for you, but a history for the whole family, and a precious heirloom for future generations.

Researching Your Family History

Researching your family history may take many months, or even years, of hard work. The best way to gather information is to try to compile the family tree step by step, generation by generation. Of course, you may find that the information is incomplete and does not come in an ordered fashion, but it is important to start off with a definite plan!

Start by finding out all you can from family members. Interview as many people as possible, and consider recording them as they speak so you have an exact transcript of their words–you never know what details may be relevant to your search.

Once you have gathered the basic information, consider widening your research to include public records. Any aspect of someone's life may have been recorded: the most common sources of information are birth certificates, marriage certificates, and death certificates, but you should also consider any or all of the following:

- Personal documents such as letters and postcards.
- Legal documents such as property deeds and wills.
- Religious records (for example, parish records often include details of baptisms and marriages).
- Newspaper cuttings, including notices of marriages, obituaries, and any other information.
- Immigration records (including lists of ships'passengers) and transportation records.
- Censuses–in many areas these are carried out on a regular basis, and may offer information on each household in the area.
- Educational records–school and college records may list their students and include details of their age, their field of study, and their achievements.
- Trade records–directories of local merchants and traders are often helpful.
- Professional records–lists of practising members of a professions such as the law, medicine, or teaching.
- Military records–these may include details of regiment, of where military personnel were based, and of war dead.
- Cemetery records and gravestone inscriptions.
- Other official records, such as voters' register, lists of members of local organizations, and similar groups of people.

There is an enormous amount of useful information relating to researching your family history available through the internet. The easiest way to start looking is simply to open a browser, such as Yahoo, AltaVista or Lycos, and type "Genealogy" in the search box. Adding the country you are interested in can help narrow the search. Repeat the process with different browsers, because each carries some links the others do not.

For example, one of the most useful sites is: http://www.familytreemaker.com/, while another good one, for American Marriage Records, is: http://www.ancestry.com/marriage/. These and similar sites lead to other sources of information about tracing family histories in almost all countries of the world.

UNITED KINGDOM

ENGLAND AND WALES

Family Records Centre
1 Myddelton Street
London EC1R 1UW, UK

Public Records Office
Ruskin Avenue, Kew
Richmond, Surrey
TW9 4DU, UK

Society of Genealogists
14 Charterhouse Buildings
Goswell Road
London EC1M 7BA, UK

SCOTLAND

General Register Office
New Register House
Edinburgh, Scotland

NORTHERN IRELAND

Public Record Office of
Northern Ireland (PRONI)
66 Balmoral Avenue
Belfast BT9 6NY, Northern Ireland

OVERSEAS

USA

Civil Reference Branch (NNRC)
National Archives Office,
Washington DC 20408

Each State of the Union keeps its own records, usually held in the State Capitol. Local libraries, religious archives and even the World Wide Web are also important sources of information. The internet is particularly useful for tracing ancestors abroad. Sources of genealogical records can be found in most countries; some are listed below. Others can be researched through the appropriate embassy or consulate.

Family History Library,
The Church of Jesus Christ of
Latter-Day Saints,
35 North West Temple,
Salt Lake City, Utah, UT 84150
tel: (801) 240 3702

The internet address for this resource as well as for Family History Centers in the USA, Canada, the British Isles, New Zealand and Australia is:
http://www.new-jerusalem.com/
genealogy/FHC/fhc.html

AUSTRALIA

Australia National Library
Parkes Place, Canberra,
2601 ACT, Australia

Australian Archives
Sandford Street, Mitchell,
Canberra 2911 ACT, Australia

CANADA

For information on birth records, contact the Registrar General's Office in each of the provinces.

GERMANY

DAGV, Schlosstrasse 12
50321 Bruhl, Germany

IRELAND

National Archives
Bishop Street, Dublin 8

ITALY

Ancetre Italiens
3 Rue de Turbigo
75001 Paris, France

NETHERLANDS

Nederlandse Genealogische
Vereniging, Postbus 976
NL-1000 AZ
Amsterdam, Netherlands

NEW ZEALAND

National Archives of
New Zealand
PO Box 12-050
Wellington 6038
New Zealand

NORWAY

Norsk Slektshistorisk Forening
Sentrum,
Postboks 59
N-0101,
Oslo
Norway

POLAND

Naczelna Archiwow Dyrekcja
(Polish National Archives)
U1 Oluga 6 Skr. Poczt
1005 00-950
Warszawa
Poland

SWEDEN

Sveriges Släktforskarförbund
(Federation of
Genealogical Societies)
Box 30222
10425 Stockholm
Sweden

THE FAMILY

Cultural Heritage

Record your family origins here. Where did your family come from? If they came from another country or area, describe why they moved and how the family came to be living where it is today.

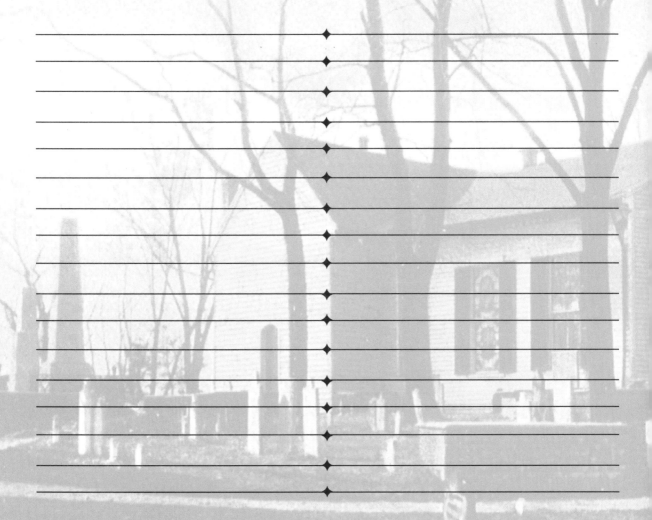

THE FAMILY

Religion And Places Of Worship

Describe your place of worship here.
Record how special religious festivals are celebrated.

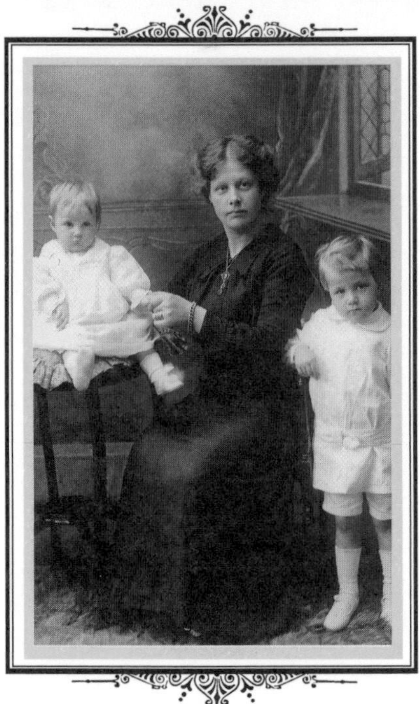

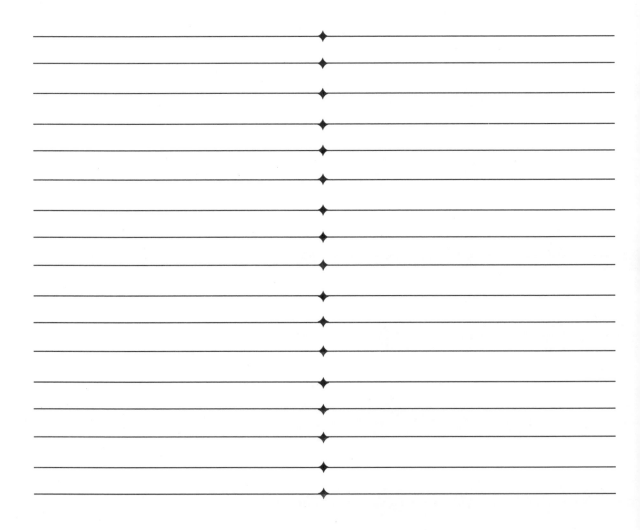

THE FAMILY

Ancestors

What do you know about your ancestors? When were they alive? Did they have special interests or hobbies, or perhaps unusual characteristics? Ask older members of the family what they remember about figures from the past. How did they dress? Did they have any favourite sayings?

THE FAMILY

Tales From The Past

Every family has a history. Find out what events shaped your family history. What effect did wars and political events have on the family? Did any family members move abroad or marry because of world events?

THE FAMILY

Military Records

Record the details of your family's military service here. Try to find out where members of your family were posted, and whether they entered into battle.

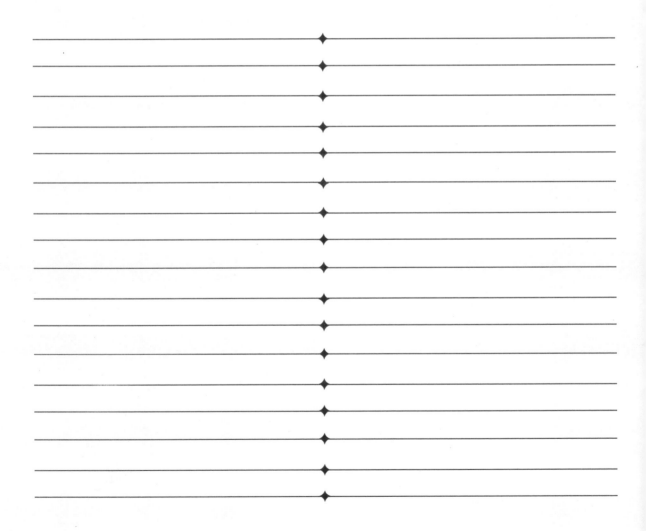

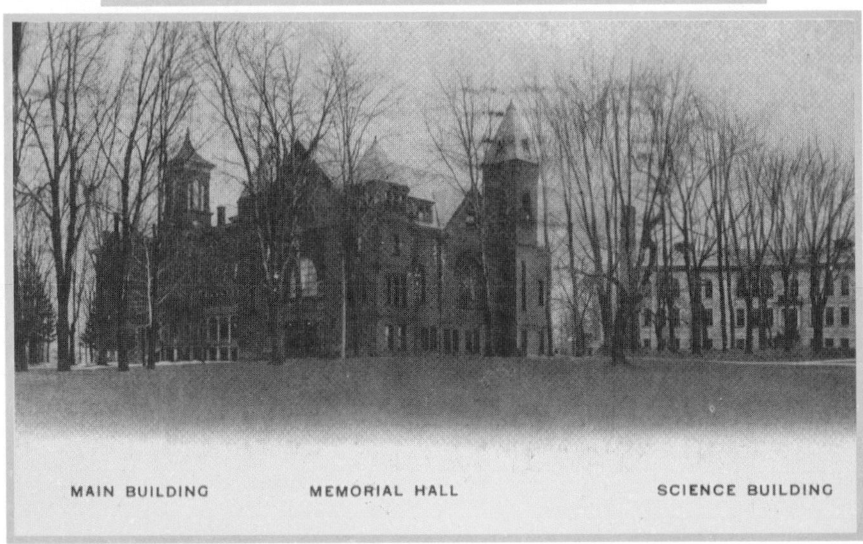
MAIN BUILDING
MEMORIAL HALL
SCIENCE BUILDING

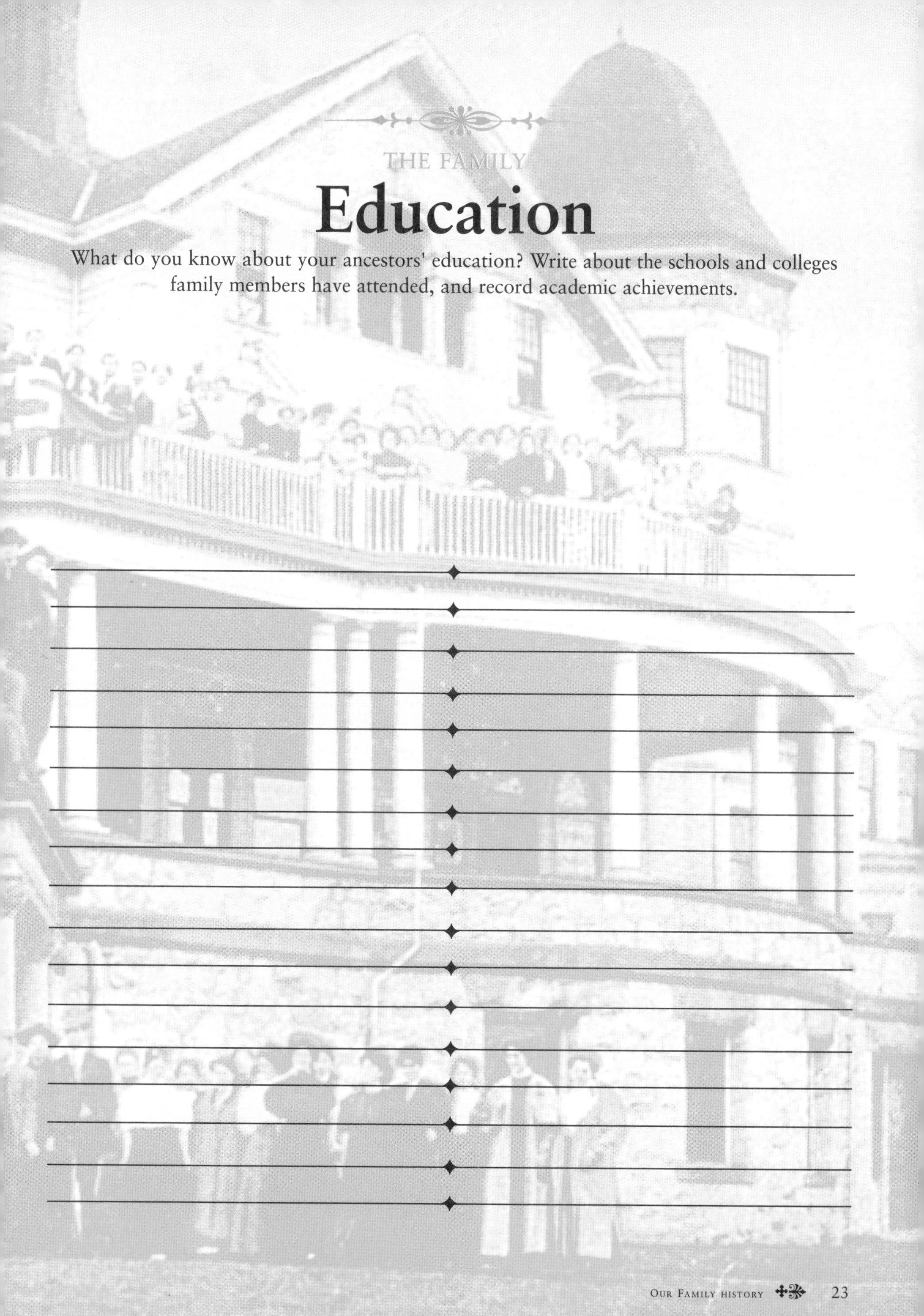

THE FAMILY

Education

What do you know about your ancestors' education? Write about the schools and colleges family members have attended, and record academic achievements.

FAMILY PROFILES

Maternal Great-Great-Grandparents

Write about your great-great-grandparents on your mother's side of the family here. Write about their childhoods, their homes, their work, their interests, their vacations ...

FULL NAME	DATE OF BIRTH

FULL NAME

DATE OF BIRTH

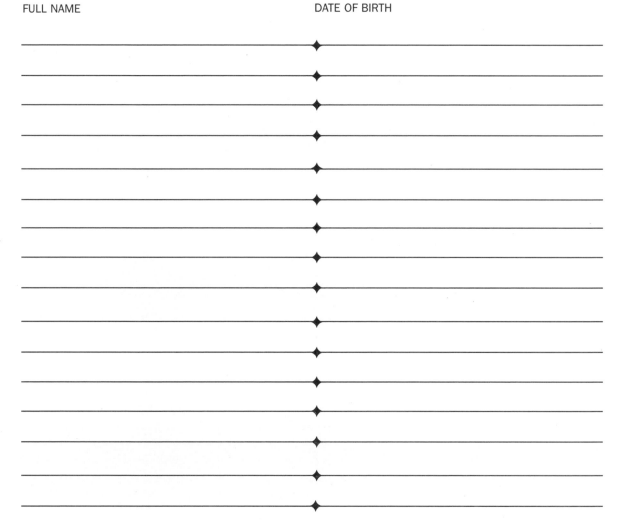

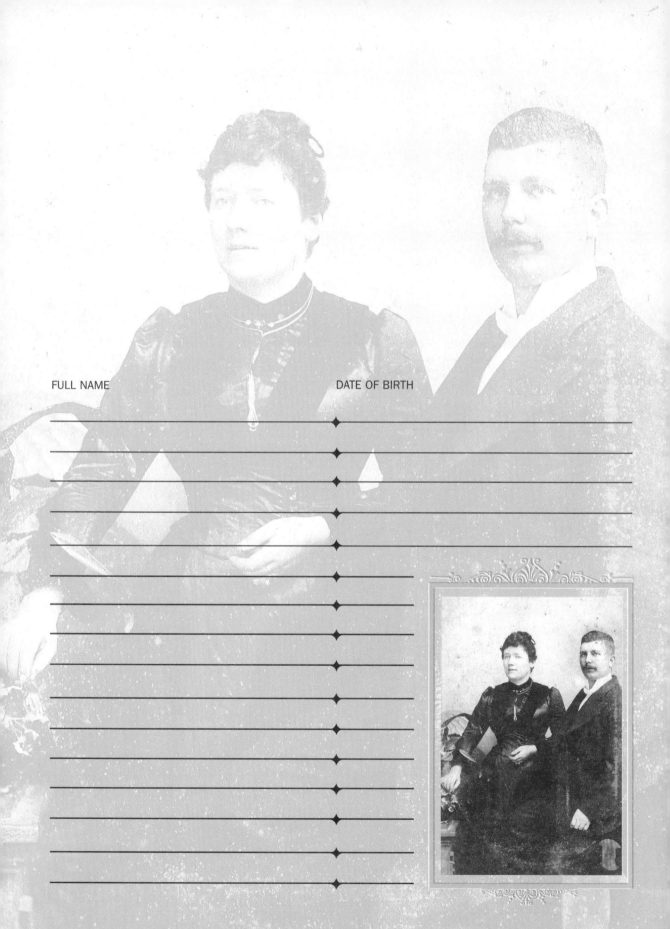

FULL NAME DATE OF BIRTH

FAMILY PROFILES

Paternal Great-Great-Grandparents

Write about your great-great-grandparents on your father's side of the family here. Write about their childhoods, their homes, their work, their interests, their vacations ...

FULL NAME	DATE OF BIRTH

FAMILY PROFILES

Maternal Great-Grandparents

Write about your great-grandparents on your mother's side of the family here. Write about their childhoods, their homes, their work, their interests, their vacations ...

FULL NAME

DATE OF BIRTH

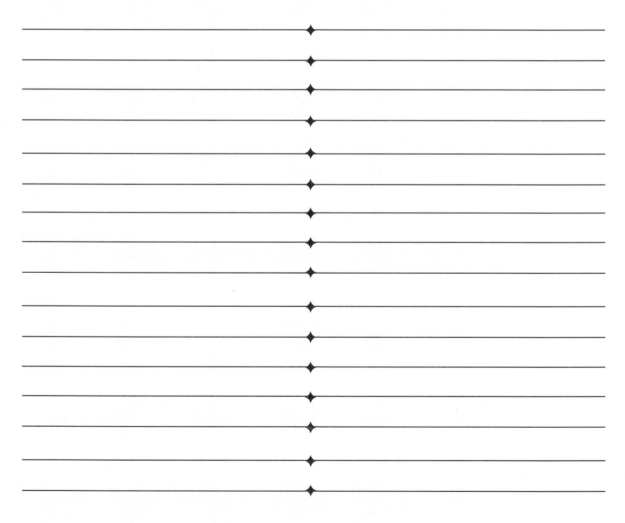

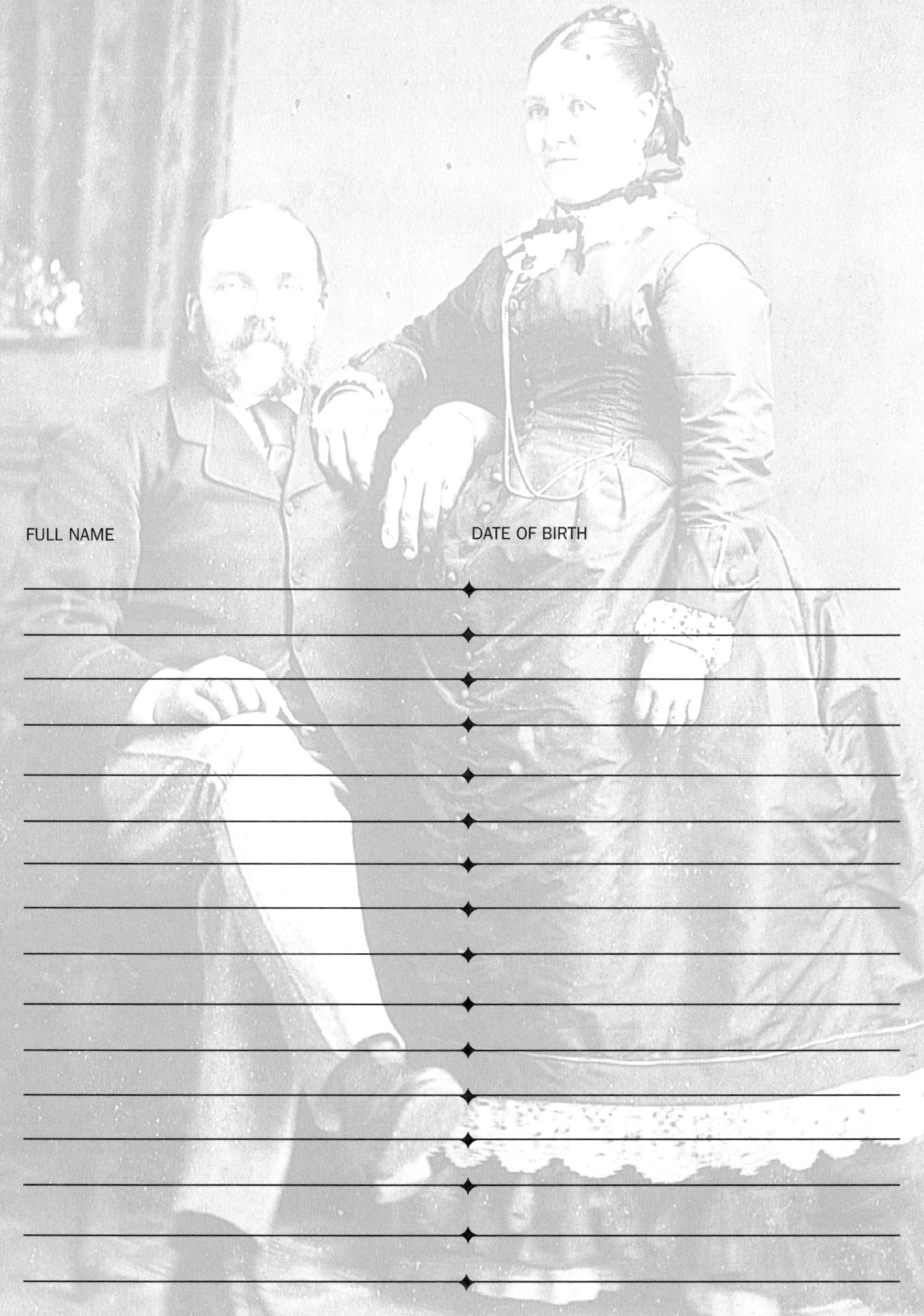

FULL NAME	DATE OF BIRTH

FAMILY PROFILES

Paternal Great-Grandparents

Write about your great-grandparents on your father's side here. Write about their childhoods, their homes, their work, their interests, their vacations ...

FULL NAME

DATE OF BIRTH

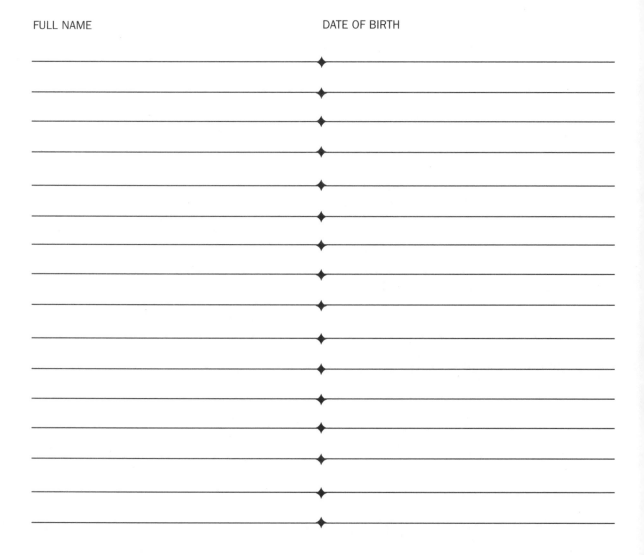

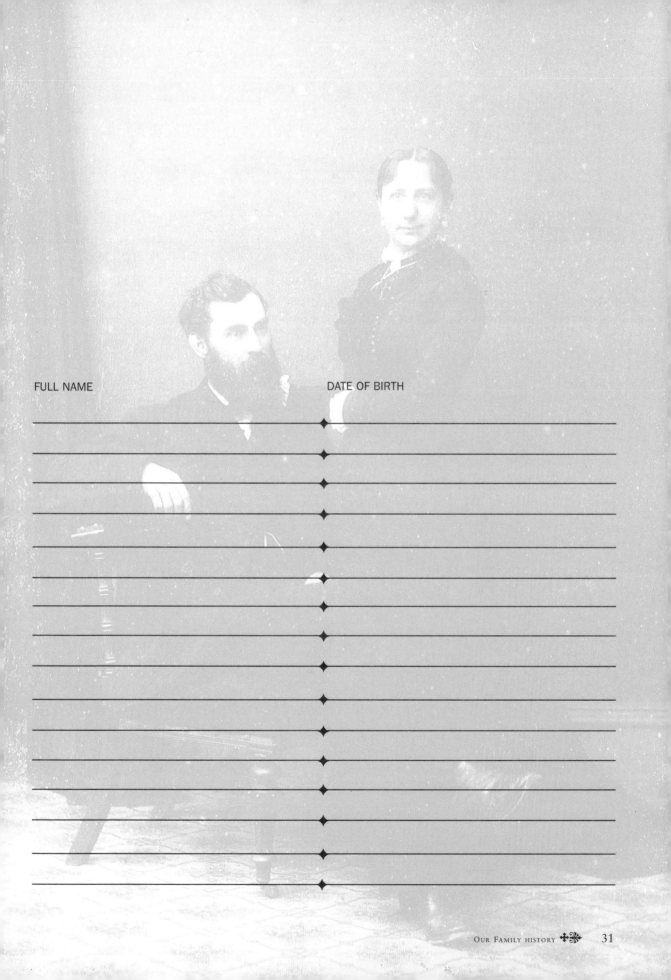

FULL NAME | DATE OF BIRTH

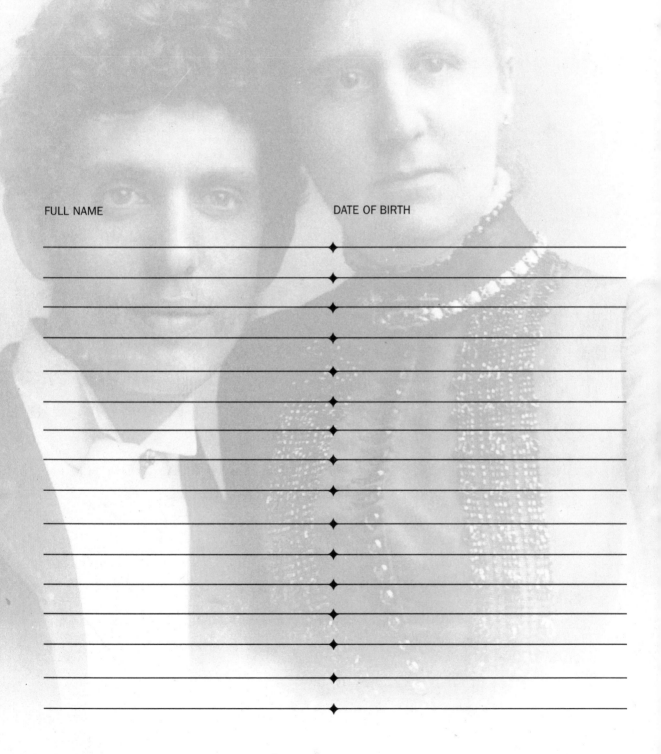

FULL NAME	DATE OF BIRTH

FAMILY PROFILES

Maternal Grandparents

This is the place to write about your maternal grandparents. How did they meet? What do they remember about their childhoods? How have technical advances changed the way they live? What do they do?

FULL NAME

DATE OF BIRTH

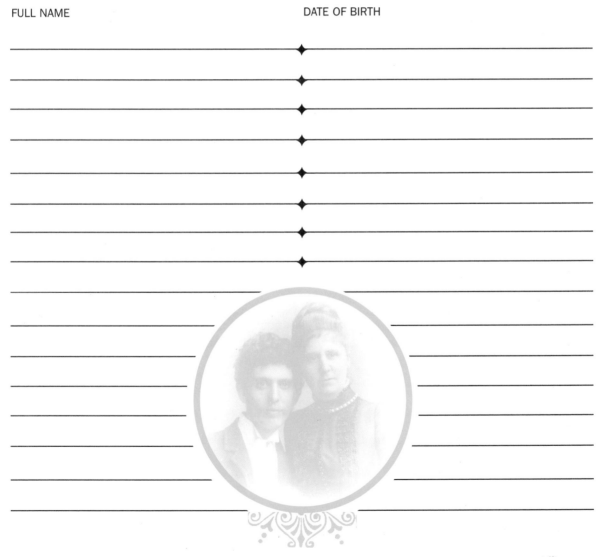

FULL NAME	DATE OF BIRTH

FAMILY PROFILES

Paternal Grandparents

This is the place to write about your paternal grandparents. How did they meet? What do they remember about their childhoods? How have technical advances changed the way they live? What do they do?

FULL NAME

DATE OF BIRTH

NAMES OF GREAT-AUNTS AND GREAT-UNCLES	DATE OF BIRTH

FAMILY PROFILES

Great-Aunts And Great-Uncles

Do any of your grandparents have brothers and sisters?
Write about them here.

NAMES OF GREAT-AUNTS AND GREAT-UNCLES	DATE OF BIRTH

FAMILY PROFILES

Parents–*mother*

How much do you know about your mother? Think what details will be interesting to future generations. What are her greatest achievements, her happiest moments, her strongest memories?

FULL NAME

DATE OF BIRTH

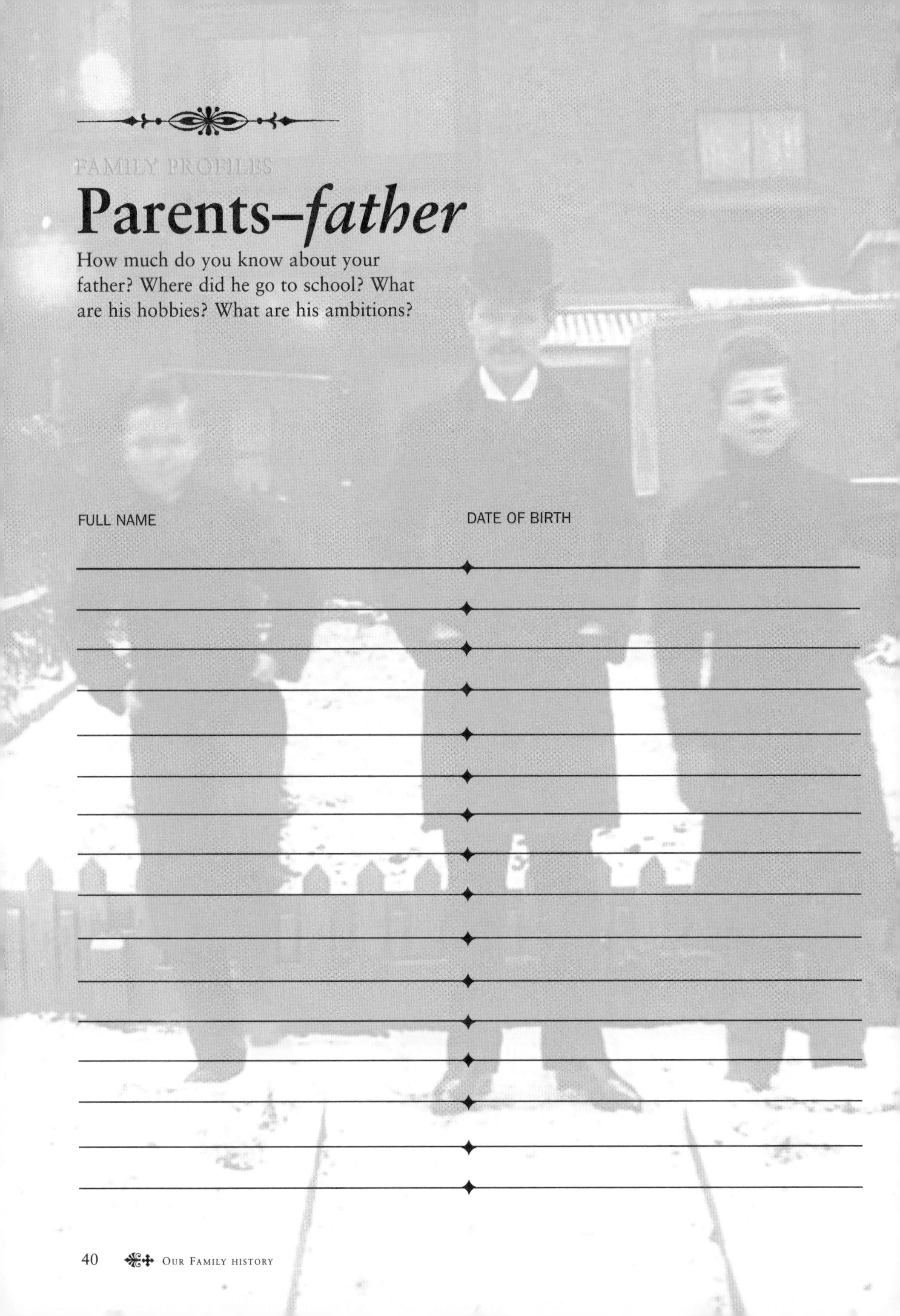

FAMILY PROFILES

Parents–*father*

How much do you know about your father? Where did he go to school? What are his hobbies? What are his ambitions?

FULL NAME

DATE OF BIRTH

FAMILY PROFILES

Sisters

How many sisters do you have?
What are they like?
What interests do they have?

FULL NAME	DATE OF BIRTH

FULL NAME	DATE OF BIRTH

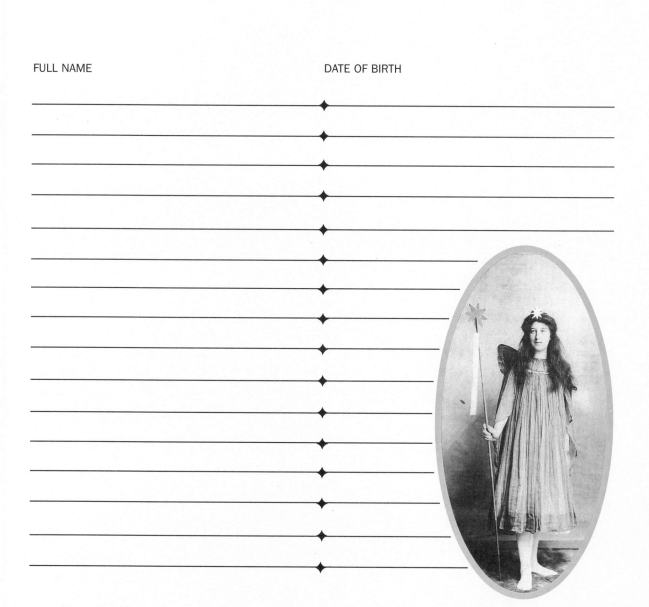

FAMILY PROFILES

Brothers

How many brothers do you have? What do they like to do? What do they hate doing? What are their ambitions?

FULL NAME OF BROTHER	DATE OF BIRTH

FAMILY PROFILES

About Me ...

This is the place to write about yourself. Why did you want to compile this history? Who is your favourite figure from your family history and why? Who do you resemble most closely in the family? What are your ambitions? What do you love and hate?

MY FULL NAME

DATE OF BIRTH

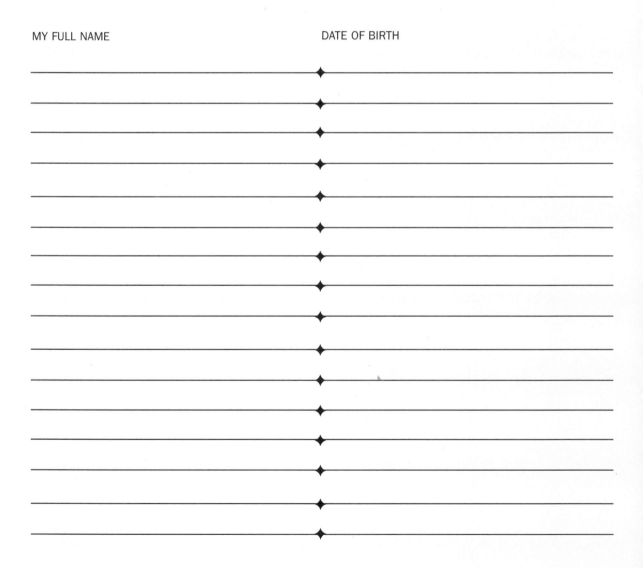

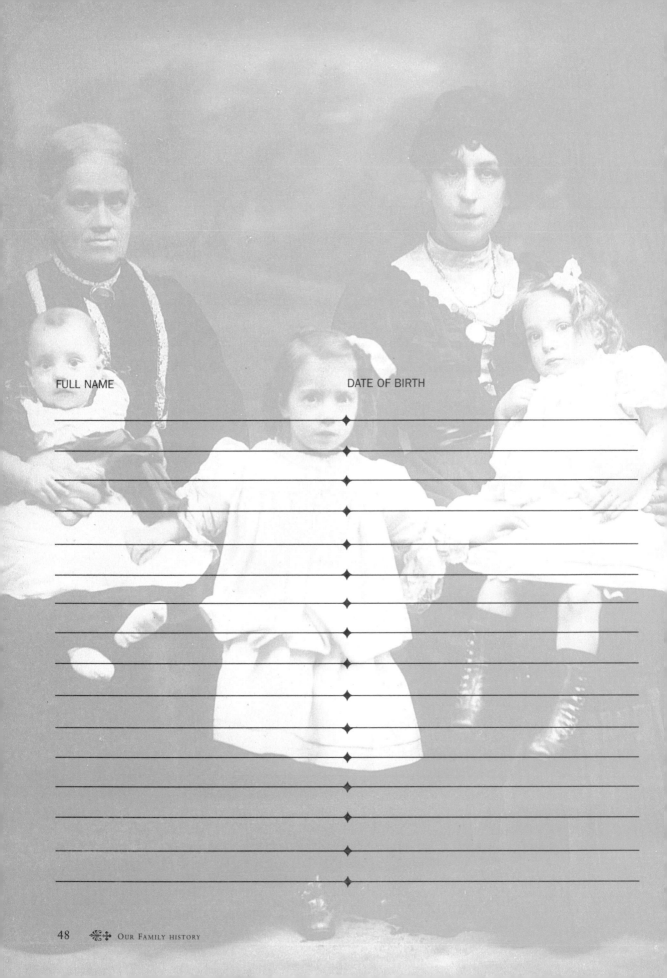

FULL NAME DATE OF BIRTH

FAMILY PROFILES

Aunts And Uncles

Do your parents have any brothers or sisters? What are they like? Ask your parents or grandparents what your aunts and uncles were like when they were younger.

FULL NAME	DATE OF BIRTH

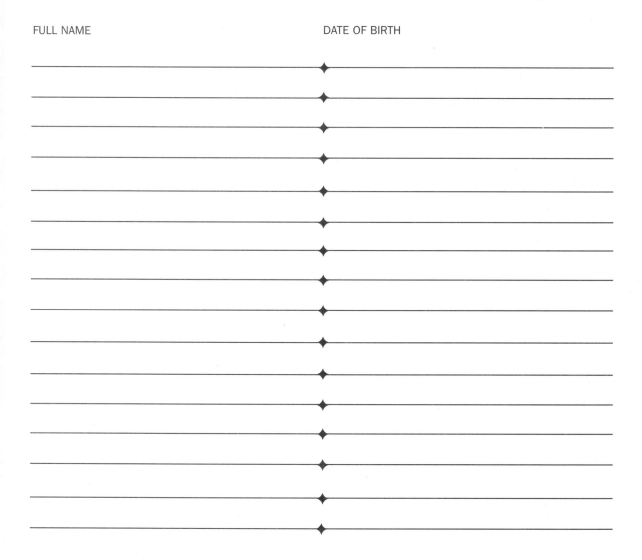

FAMILY PROFILES

Cousins

Do your uncles and aunts have any children?
Are they older or younger than you?
Do you see them often?

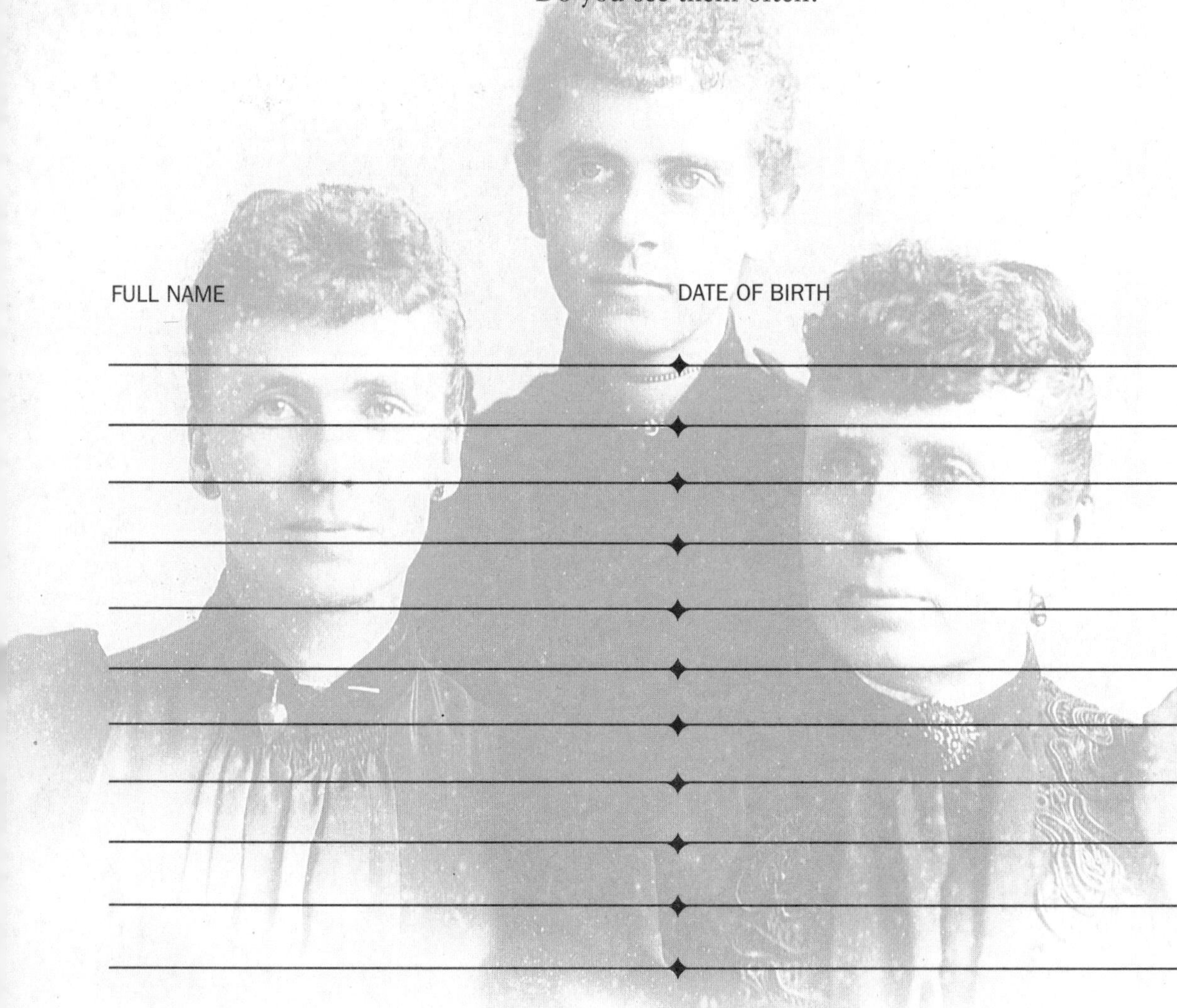

FULL NAME	DATE OF BIRTH

FULL NAME	DATE OF BIRTH

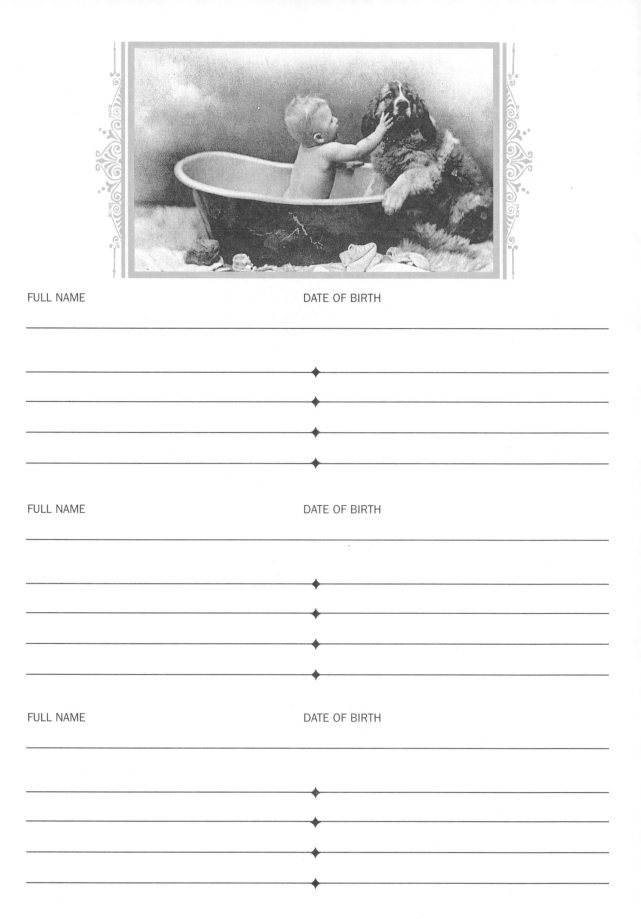

FULL NAME DATE OF BIRTH

FULL NAME DATE OF BIRTH

FULL NAME DATE OF BIRTH

FAMILY PROFILES

New Arrivals

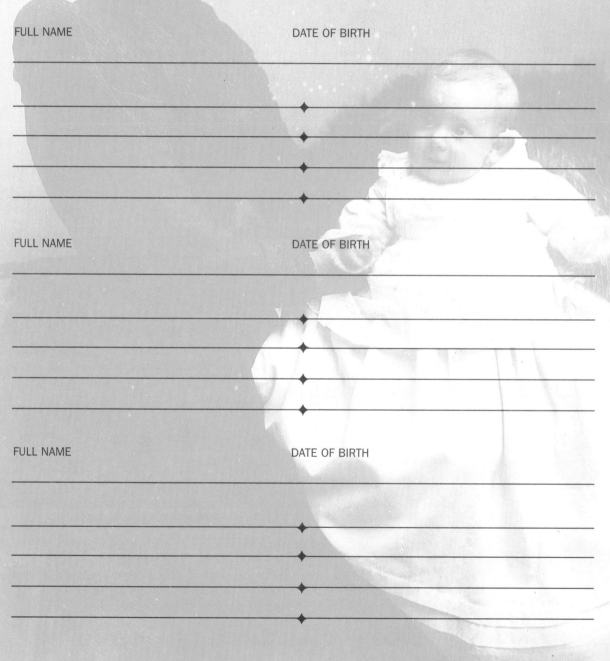

This is the place to write about babies born to the family. Write their dates of birth, and how much they weighed. Who do they most look like in the family?

FULL NAME DATE OF BIRTH

FULL NAME DATE OF BIRTH

FULL NAME DATE OF BIRTH

FULL NAME

DATE OF BIRTH

FULL NAME

DATE OF BIRTH

FULL NAME

DATE OF BIRTH

FAMILY PROFILES

New Arrivals

FULL NAME DATE OF BIRTH

FULL NAME DATE OF BIRTH

FULL NAME DATE OF BIRTH

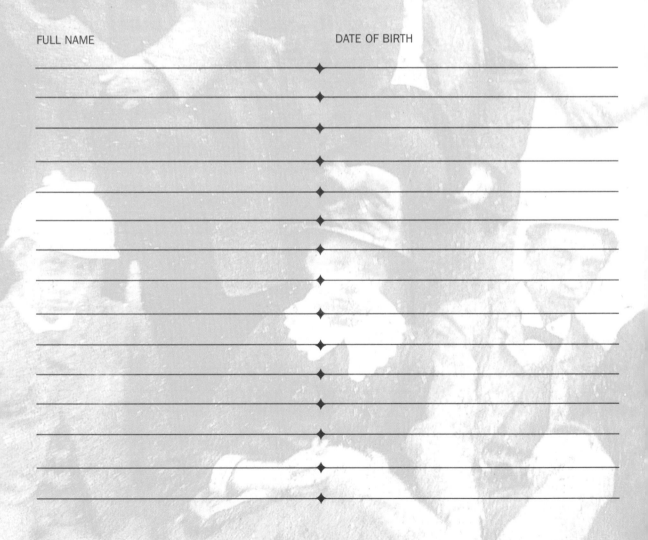

SPECIAL OCCASIONS

Extended Family

Write about your extended family here. What do you know about their childhoods, their homes, their work, their interests, their vacations ...

FULL NAME	DATE OF BIRTH

SPECIAL OCCASIONS

Family Weddings

Write about family weddings here. What did the bride wear? Who were the bridesmaids? Where was the wedding held? Where did the couple go on their honeymoon?

BRIDE'S NAME

BRIDEGROOM'S NAME

DATE OF WEDDING

BRIDE'S NAME

BRIDEGROOM'S NAME

DATE OF WEDDING

SPECIAL OCCASIONS

Family Weddings

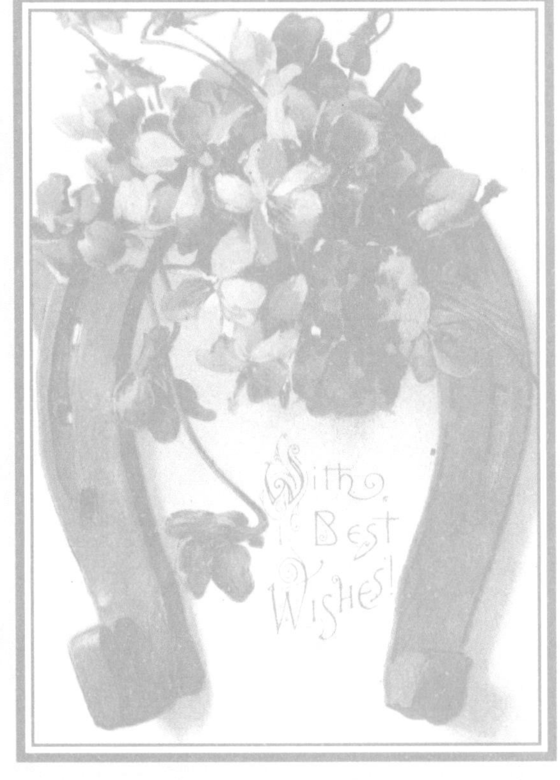

BRIDE'S NAME

BRIDEGROOM'S NAME

DATE OF WEDDING

BRIDE'S NAME

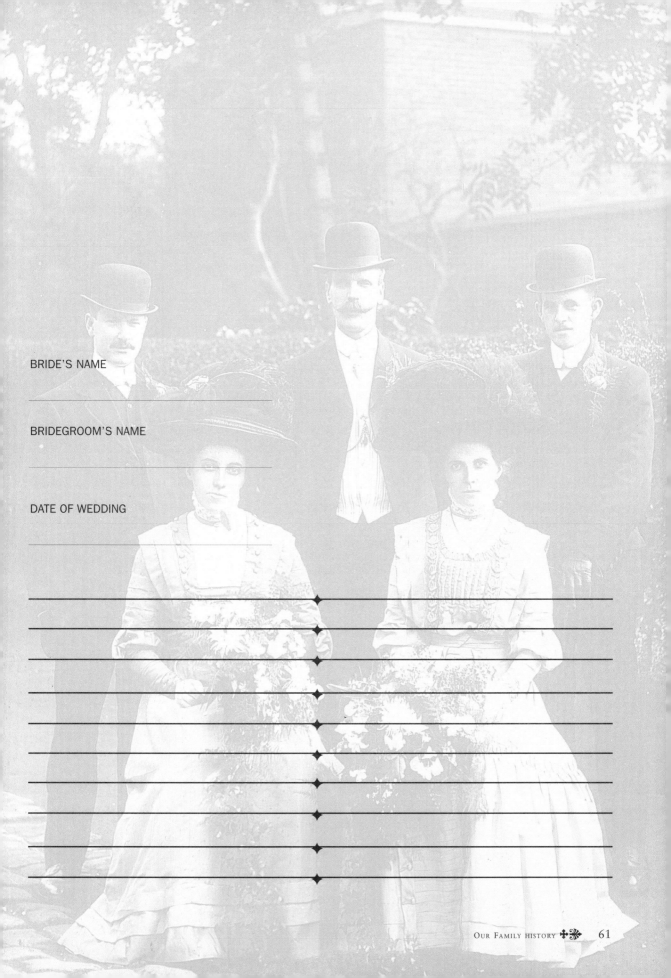

BRIDEGROOM'S NAME

DATE OF WEDDING

SPECIAL OCCASIONS

Other Family Gatherings

Write about other family gatherings here. These could include religious ceremonies, anniversaries, and birthday parties. Who was there? What did you eat?

SPECIAL OCCASIONS

Vacations

Does your family go to a special place on vacation? How do you get there? Which family vacation have you enjoyed best? Try to remember any funny things that happened on your vacation.

OUR FAMILY VACATIONS

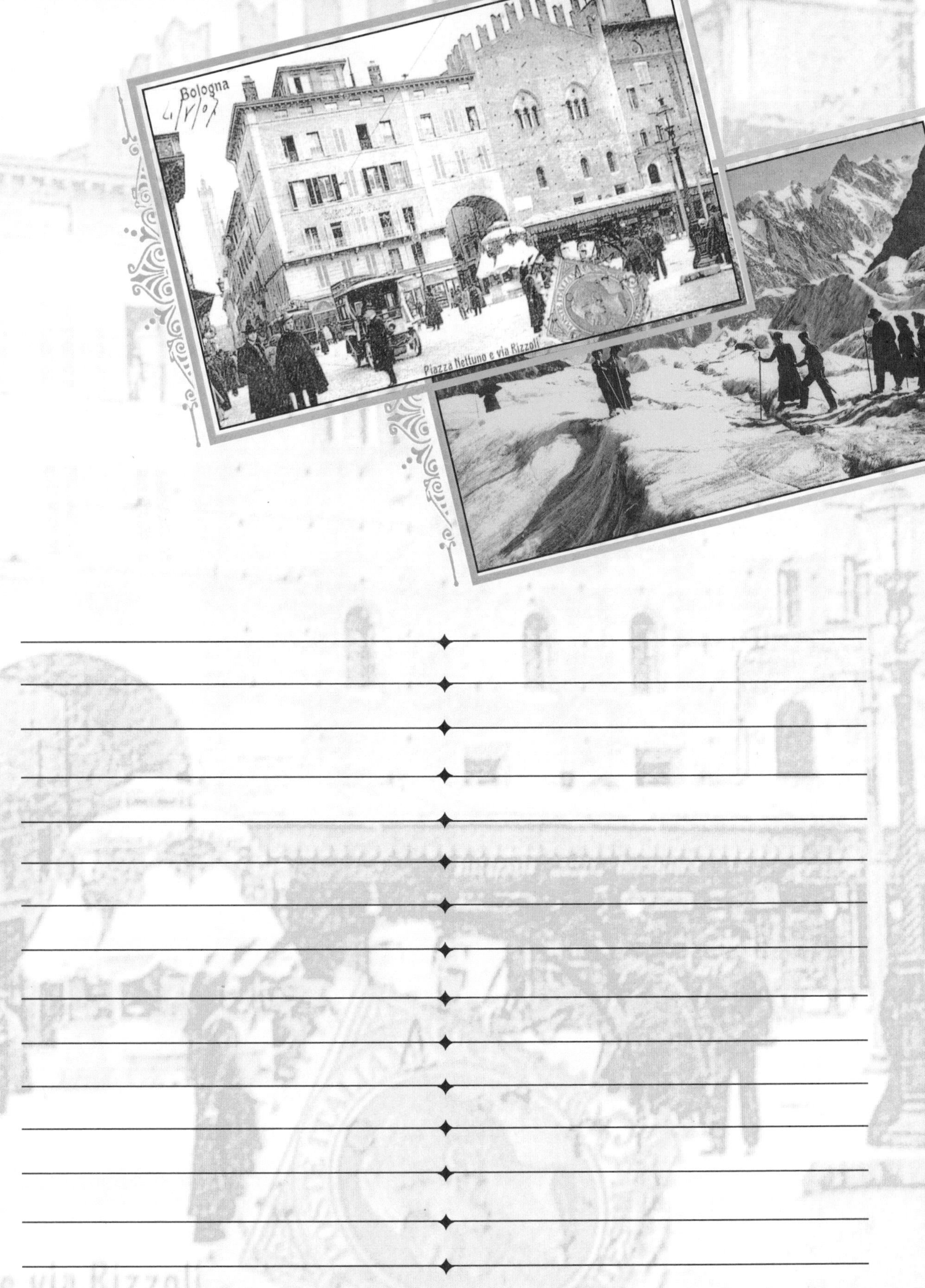
Bologna
Piazza Nettuno e via Rizzoli

SPECIAL OCCASIONS

Holidays

OUR FAMILY HOLIDAYS

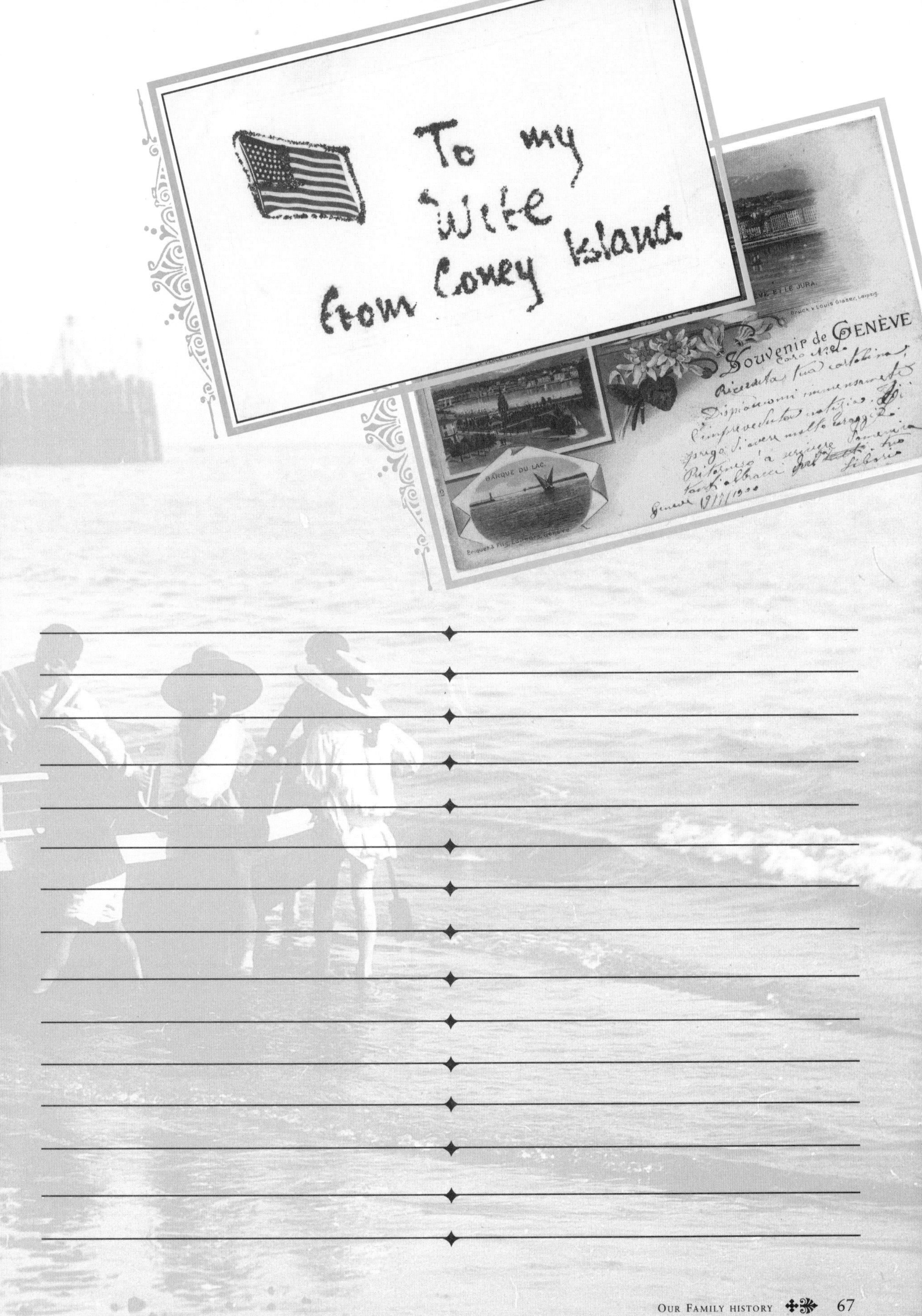
To my Wife from Coney Island
Souvenir de GENÈVE
BARQUE DU LAC

SPECIAL OCCASIONS

Family Achievements

Write about the family's proudest moments here. Have any family figures had great success in business, excelled in music, or been awarded a prize? Has anyone in your family passed exams recently or done something very brave?

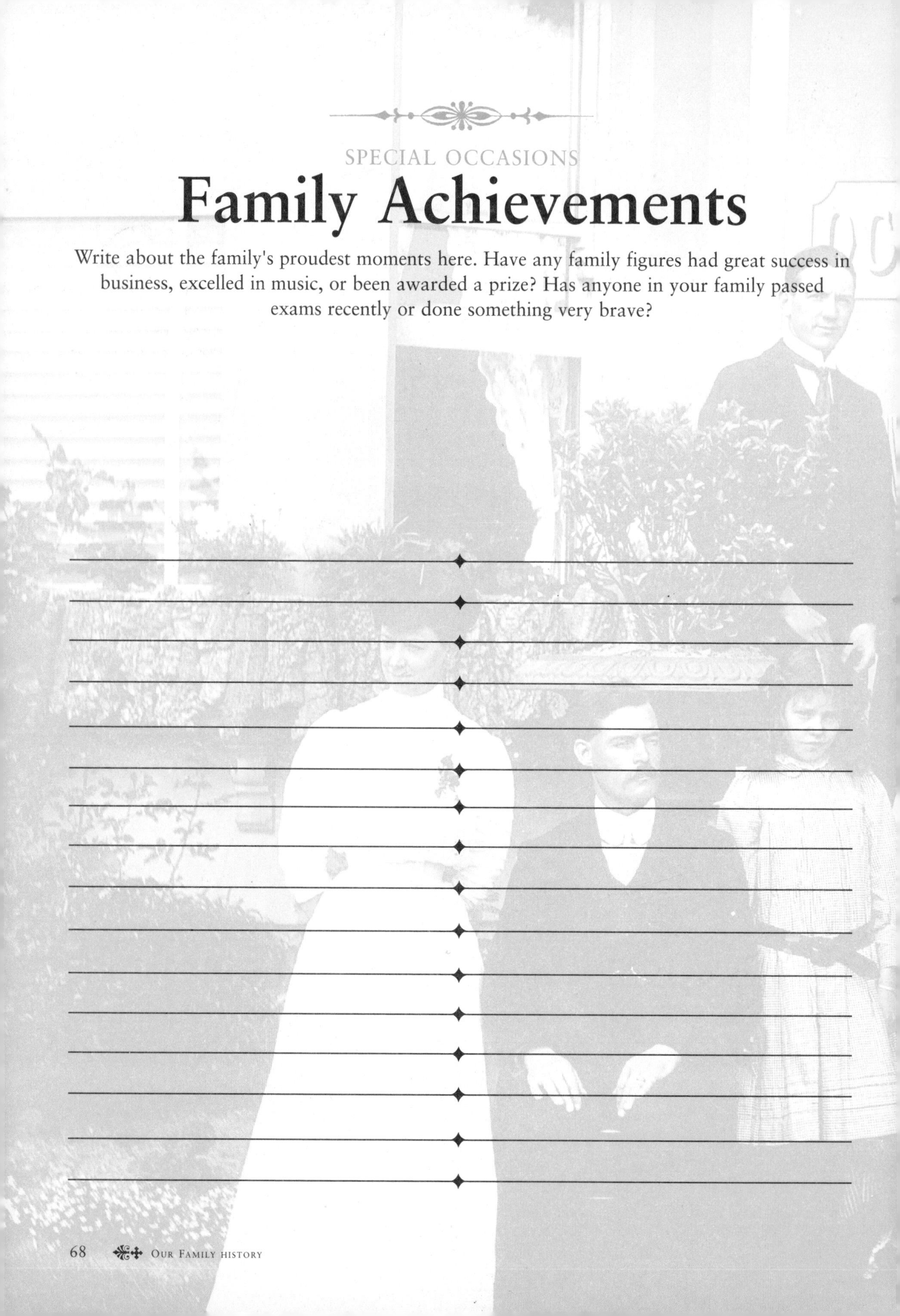

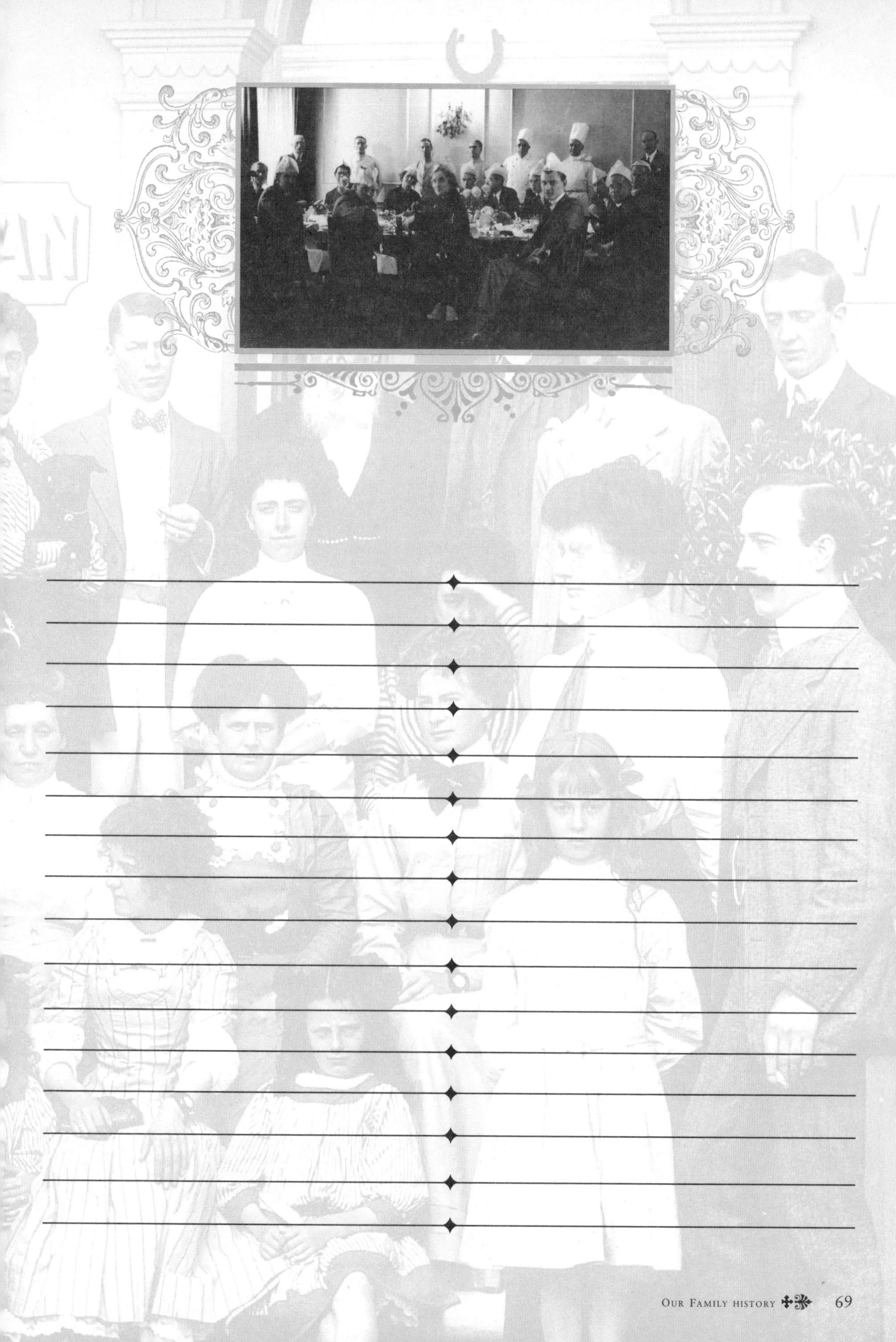

SPECIAL OCCASIONS

Favorite Family Outings

Family outings and excursions should be recorded here.
Where did you go? Who was there? What did you see?

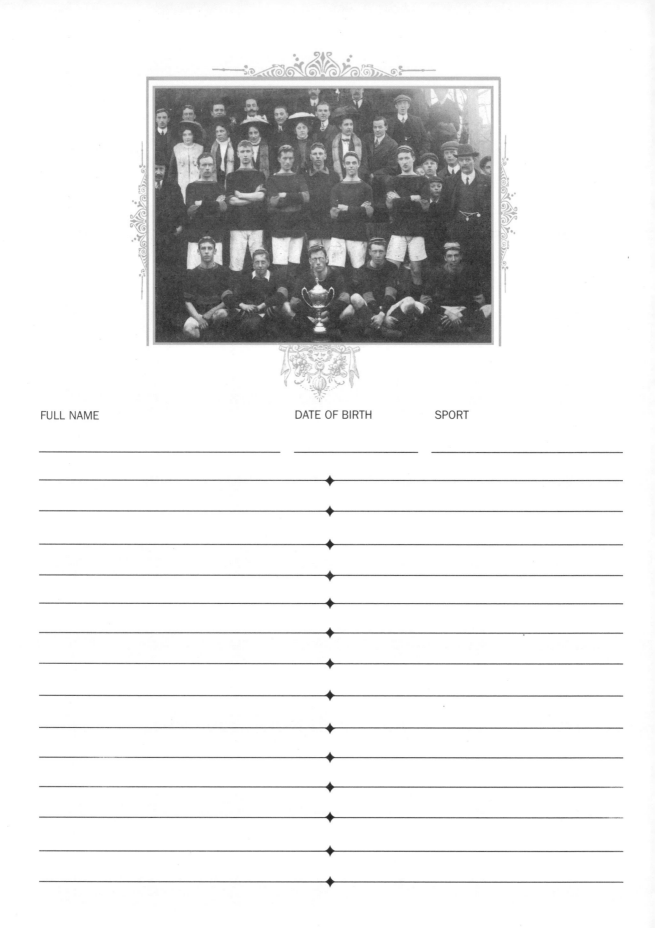

FULL NAME | DATE OF BIRTH | SPORT

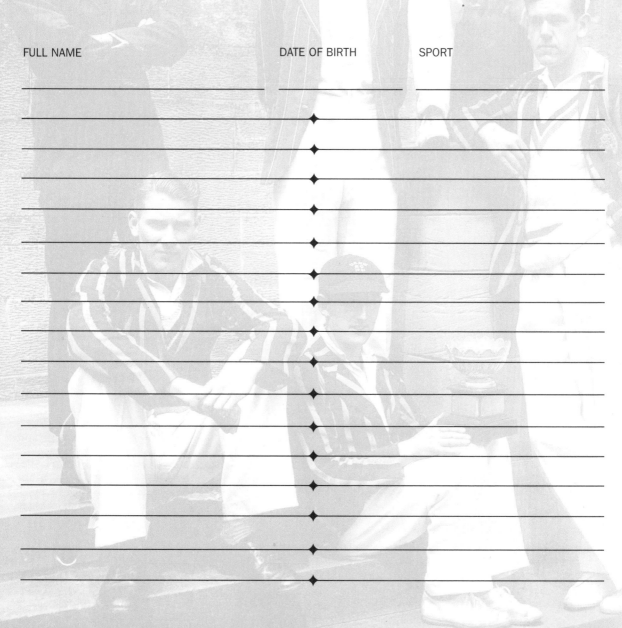

SPECIAL OCCASIONS

Sport

Do you have any great sportsmen or sportswomen in your family? In which sport does any family member have special skills or interests?

FULL NAME	DATE OF BIRTH	SPORT

SPECIAL OCCASIONS

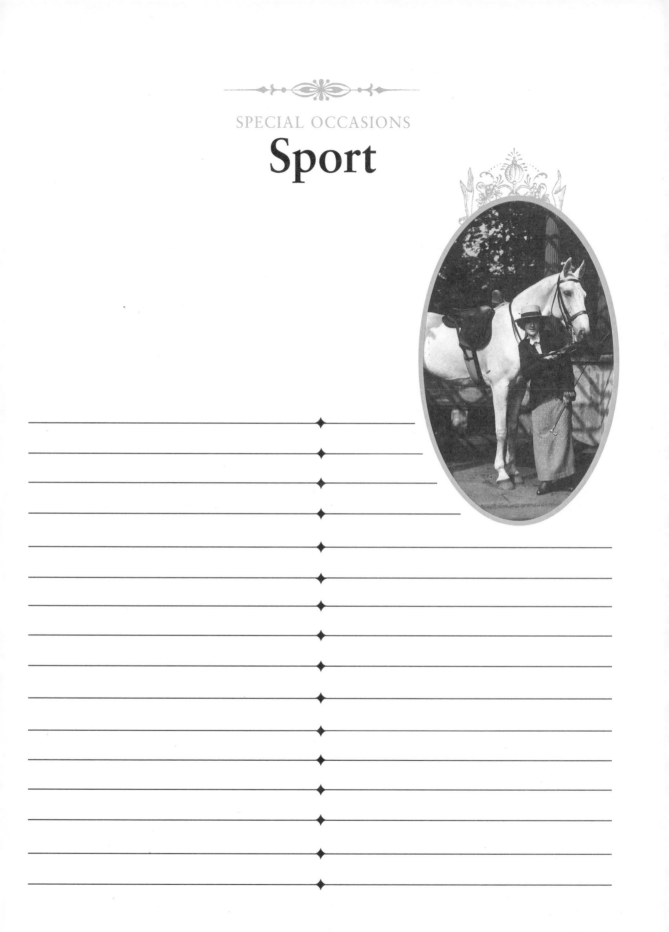

Sport

CUTTINGS

nd this also has to be
We are said to be a
et to do before we can
as we are, we are not
cally, not free to teach
good and cheap litera-
. Our people are, in
e our Government is
ught to be taxed, and
which prevents or di-
ned, is money lost, and
g knowledge it has to
s; and in all the multi-
pauperism and crimi-

consideration of the
Advertisements. We
tention of all interested
n the paper manufac-
rm lies at the root of
ss it is to write or sell
l them, will join their
in this peaceful agita-
or this or the coming
on shall be ignorant.

DINARY.

n our Journal; but neither
sport than was witnessed in
that of "a real Stag-Hunt"
About two o'clock in the
onished at the unusual sight
in the direction of Somers
ved by one solitary rider and
hard day's work. The meet
hence, in a circuitous route,
Coldfalls Wood, and passed
Town by Brewer-street, and
stead-street, finally crossing
ches. He here made a bolt
into Burton-crescent; but,
at the number of vehicles
ront of the house of Messrs.
the shop door open, he
cured. The strange scene

them, be in your canton or not, as also on other measures
in execution of the present circular, and of that of the 1
As regards the other refugee leaders named in the circu
vember, whose residence is known to you, you are inv
calculated to hasten the departure from Switzerland of su
in your canton. You will also be kind enough to mak
the present month, a report on the result of the measure
prescribed in consequence of this invitation."

This question of the refugees appears to be fraught w
quences to Switzerland. It appears that Prussia and Aus
Federal Government that, in order to reduce their arm
occupy Switzerland, and expel the whole of the refugees, w
of agitation. These two Powers declare they have come
with Russia as to the occupation of the German cantons;
occupy the French cantons she can do so; if not, these
said that Piedmont is also agreed with them respecting th
refugees are better received in the canton of Vaud than

UNITED STATES.

Advices from New York to the 25th ult. have been r
tain no news of interest.

A resolution had been introduced into Congress to c
presenting some suitable memorial to Captain Cook fo
rescuing the passengers on board the *Caleb Grimshaw*.

The bill in relation to the re-capture of futigive slave
deration. The case of Colonel Webb had been postpon
had on the Austrian resolutions of General Cass. It wa
28th ultimo.

The Hungarian refugees had dined with General Taylo
No further intelligence from California had been recei

Important Discovery.—Mr. Smith, of Dean
shire, has made an important discovery in the treatmen
whereby the fleece of the living animal is rendered repell
and cheap process; so that the sheep are defended from
wet, whilst the natural emanations from the body rema
growth and quality of the wool are improved. The effec
has been practically tested on some of the most expose
land, and with singular success. This process, it is ex
supersede the laying with tar, and butter, and other sal
cost, whilst the wool will be preserved white and pure.
salving of sheep hitherto has been applied chiefly to floc
exposed situations only, it is believed that the new mo
found beneficial to flocks on the most sheltered and sout
it will go far to prevent or mitigate that destructive dis
neither more nor less than dysentery, caused by the cont
whereby the fleeces of the sheep become soaked with rai
effect as is produced on man by wet clothing. It is a
mode of treatment will lead to the successful introductio
and the Alpaca, which are known to have suffered from
weather in this country.

The remains of the persons who were unfortuna
pier at Sunderland, in endeavouring to save the crew of a
were interred in Sunderland churchyard on Sunday afte

FAMILY STORIES

The Family In The News

Do you have any newspaper cuttings about the family? Older members of the family may have newspaper clippings from the past. Do you have anyone famous in the family?

FAMILY STORIES

Family Traditions

Are there any traditions particular to your family? Do you have family gatherings at certain times? Are there any tales or recipes that have been passed down from generation to generation?

But we hae meat and we can eat,
Sae let the Lord be thankit.
Burns
725

FAMILY STORIES

Events That Changed Our Family History

Wars, natural disasters, economic crises or unexpected success can have a huge impact on a family. Describe the momentous events that have affected your family.

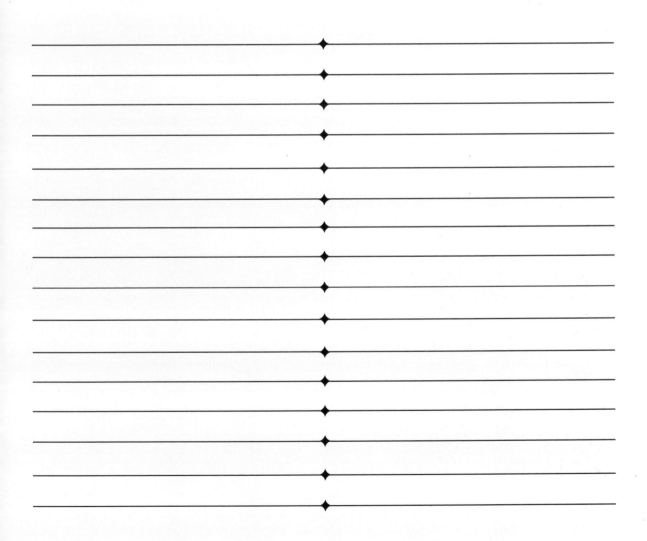

FAMILY STORIES

How Did Your Parents Meet?

Write down the circumstances which brought your parents together. Did they like each other when they first met?

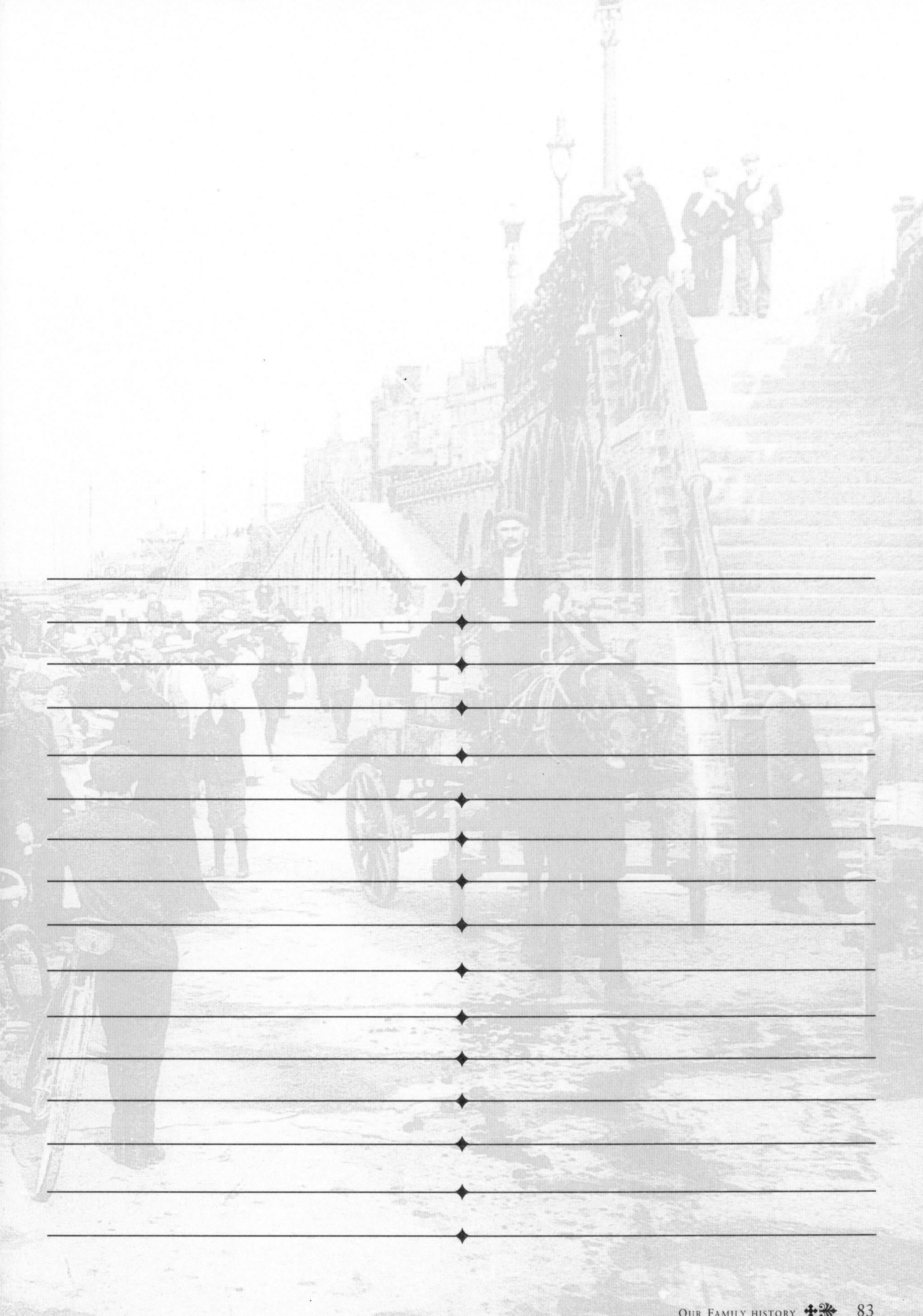

FAMILY STORIES

Eccentric Family Figures

Every family has some eccentric figures. This is the place to write about the colourful characters in your family. What makes them unusual? Write about an incident that illustrates their behaviour.

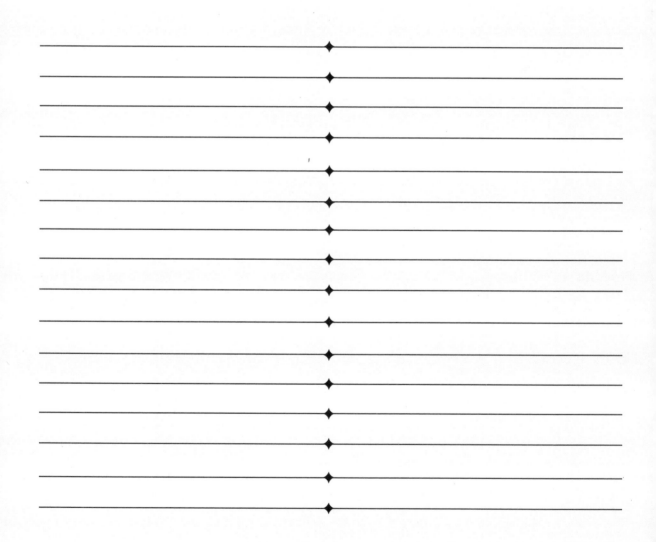

Family Jokes

Write family jokes in here. What is everyone's favourite joke? Are there any "in jokes" that only people in your family understand?

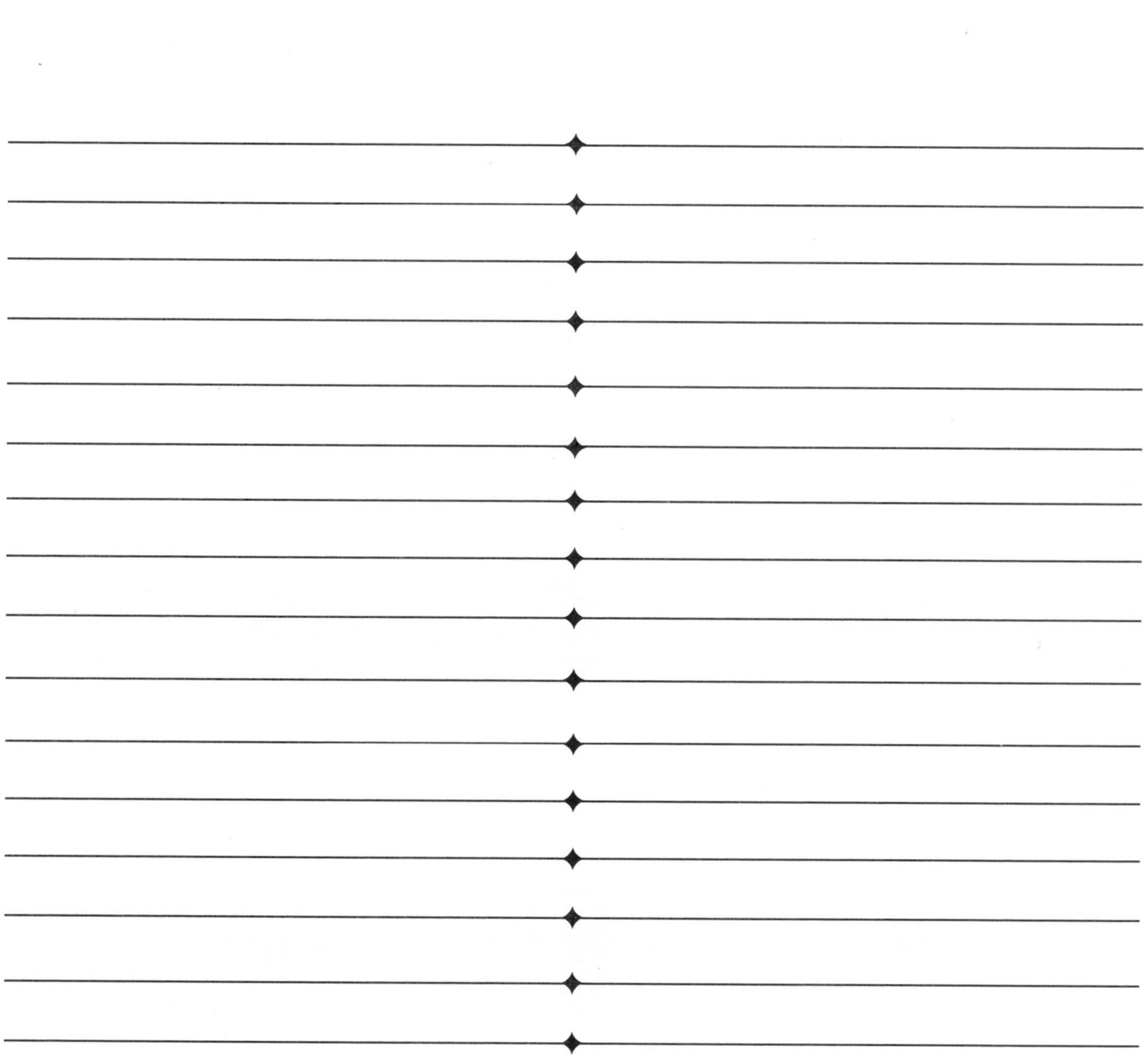

FAMILY STORIES

Amusing Family Anecdotes

Family histories include family stories. What funny things have happened over the years? Remember, someone may read this album in a few generations, so you must explain who all the characters in the story are, and where the events took place.

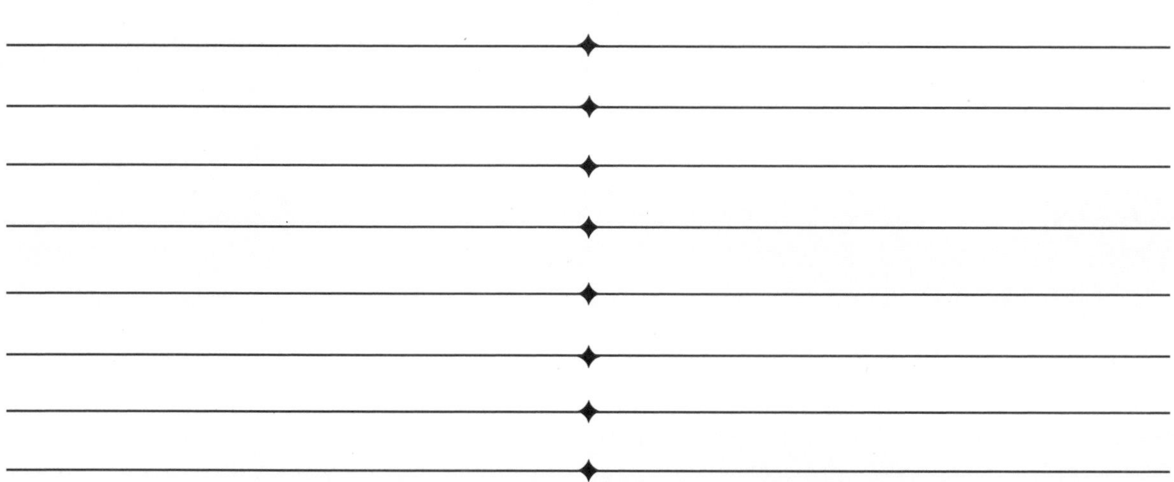

FAMILY STORIES

Embarrassing Stories

Are there any stories that embarrassed the whole family or a family member? We all say something we don't mean, or do something clumsy at some time. Write the funniest moments here.

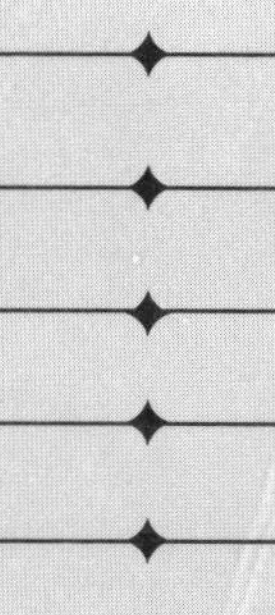

FAMILY STORIES

Tales Of Travel And Exploration

Has anyone in your family traveled the world, or even explored an area near to where they live? Who are the great explorers of the family? Try to find out all about their journeys–how did they reach their destination, where did they stay, what did they discover there?

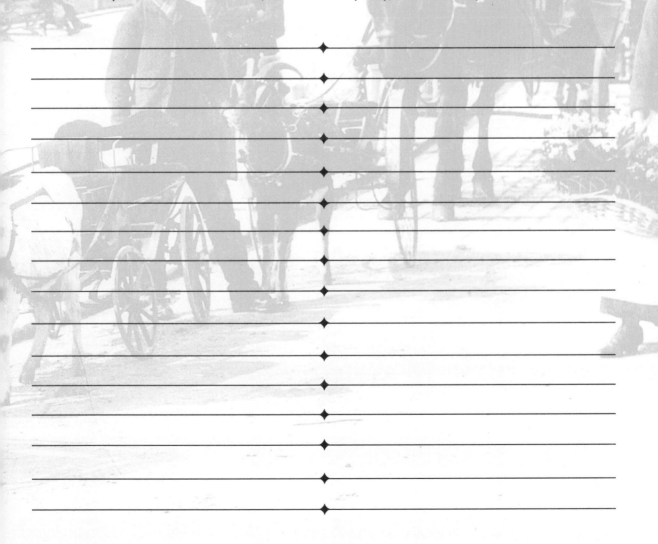

Family Friends and Neighbours

Some people are so close to the family that they are almost like one of the family. Were there any very close family friends of your grandparents or great-grandparents who are remembered in the family? Do you have neighbours where you live? Is there anyone who is a close friend of all the family?

Baby's Guardian.

FAMILY FRIENDS

Family Pets

Describe your family pets here. What are their names? How old are they? Do older members of the family remember pets from their childhood? What is the strangest pet anyone in the family has had?

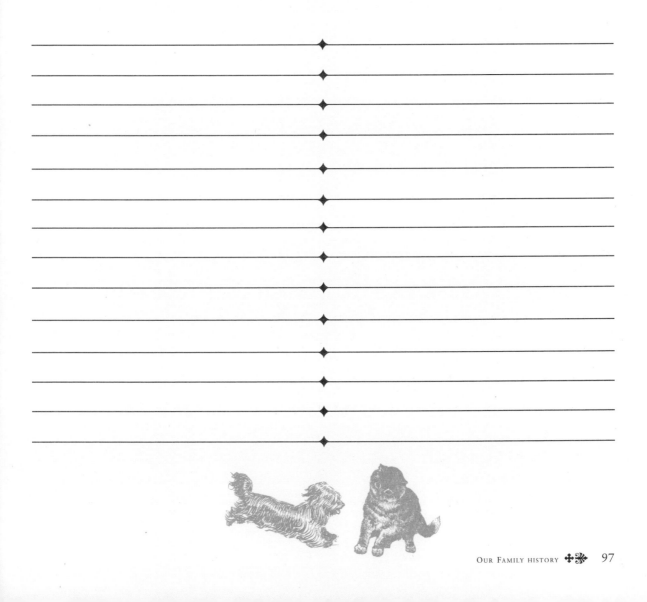

FAMILY FRIENDS

Family Pets

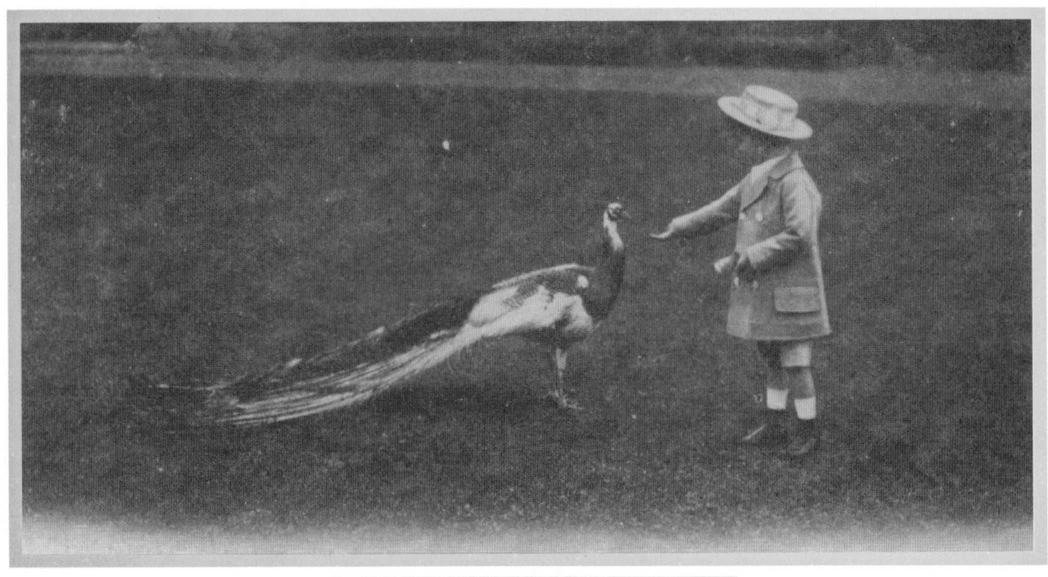

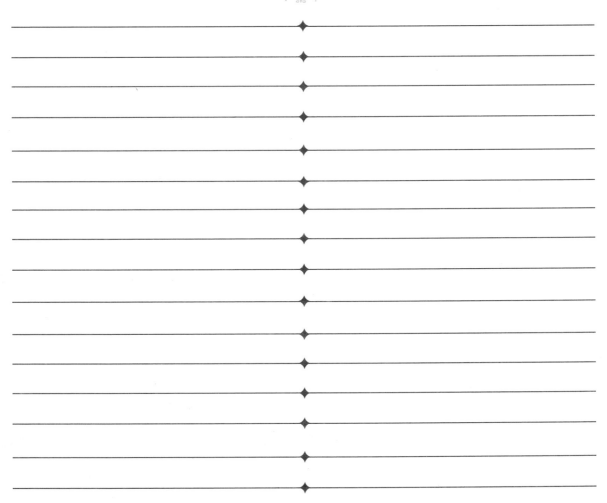

FAMILY BELONGINGS

The Family Home

The family home is an important place. Write about it here. Do you know when it was built? What improvements have your family made? Are there any records of the houses in which your ancestors lived? Get older members of the family to describe where they were brought up.

ADDRESS

DATE WE MOVED IN DATE WE LEFT

ADDRESS

DATE WE MOVED IN DATE WE LEFT

ADDRESS

DATE WE MOVED IN DATE WE LEFT

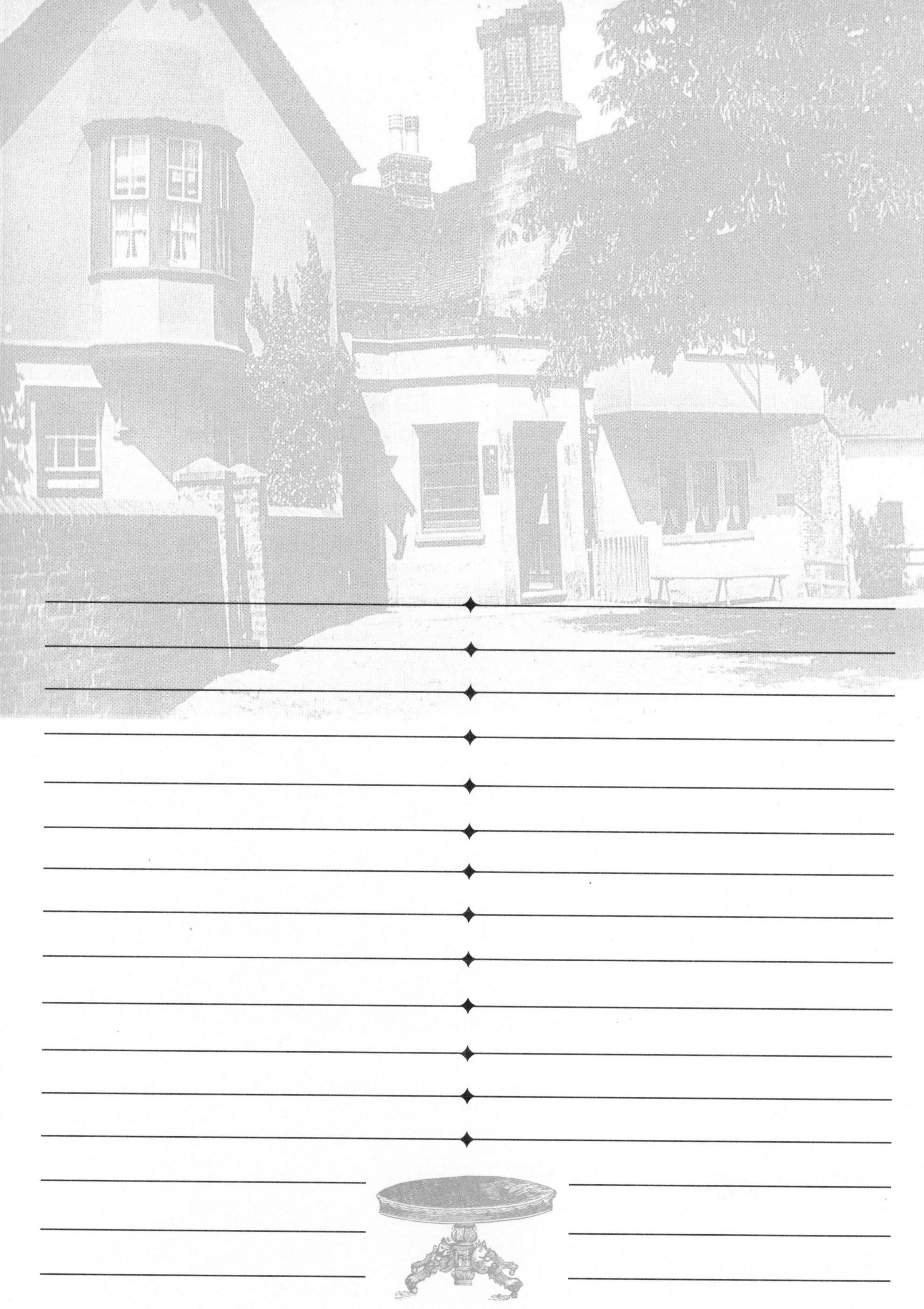

FAMILY BELONGINGS

The Family Home

ADDRESS

DATE WE MOVED IN DATE WE LEFT

ADDRESS

DATE WE MOVED IN DATE WE LEFT

ADDRESS

DATE WE MOVED IN DATE WE LEFT

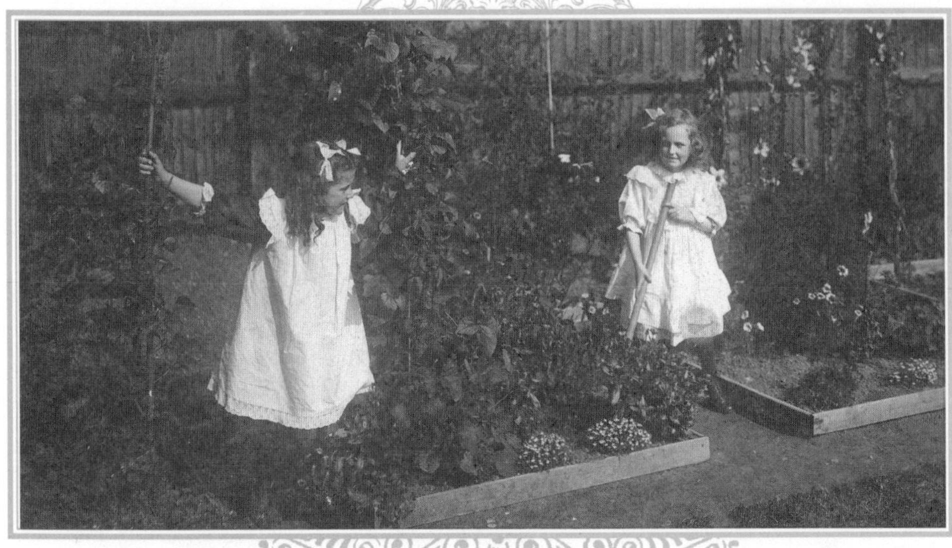

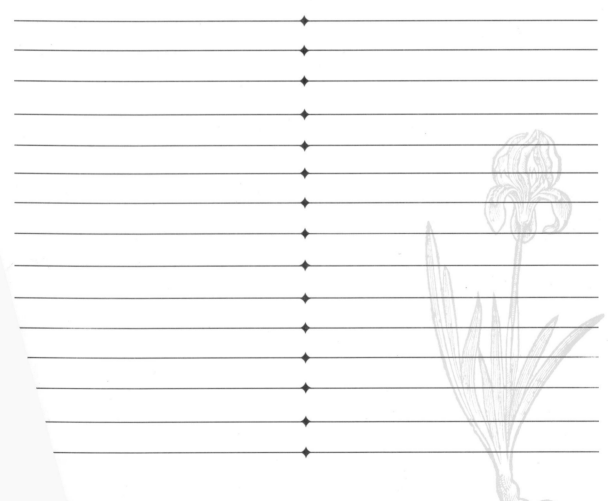

FAMILY BELONGINGS

The Garden

Describe the family garden. What grows there?
What special memories do family members have of the garden?
What interesting or unusual flowers, plants, and trees have grown in your family garden?
Who planted them?

FAMILY BELONGINGS

The Garden

Plan your own special family garden.

FAMILY BELONGINGS

Transport

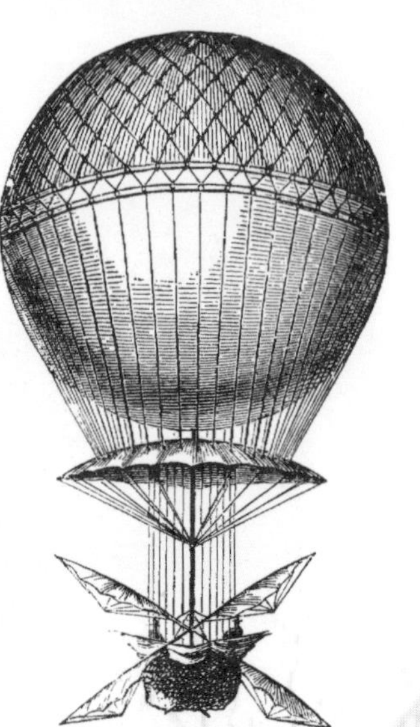

Does your family have a car, a van, a bicycle, even an aeroplane? Who was the first person in your family to have a car? What is the most unusual means of transport used by a member of your family?

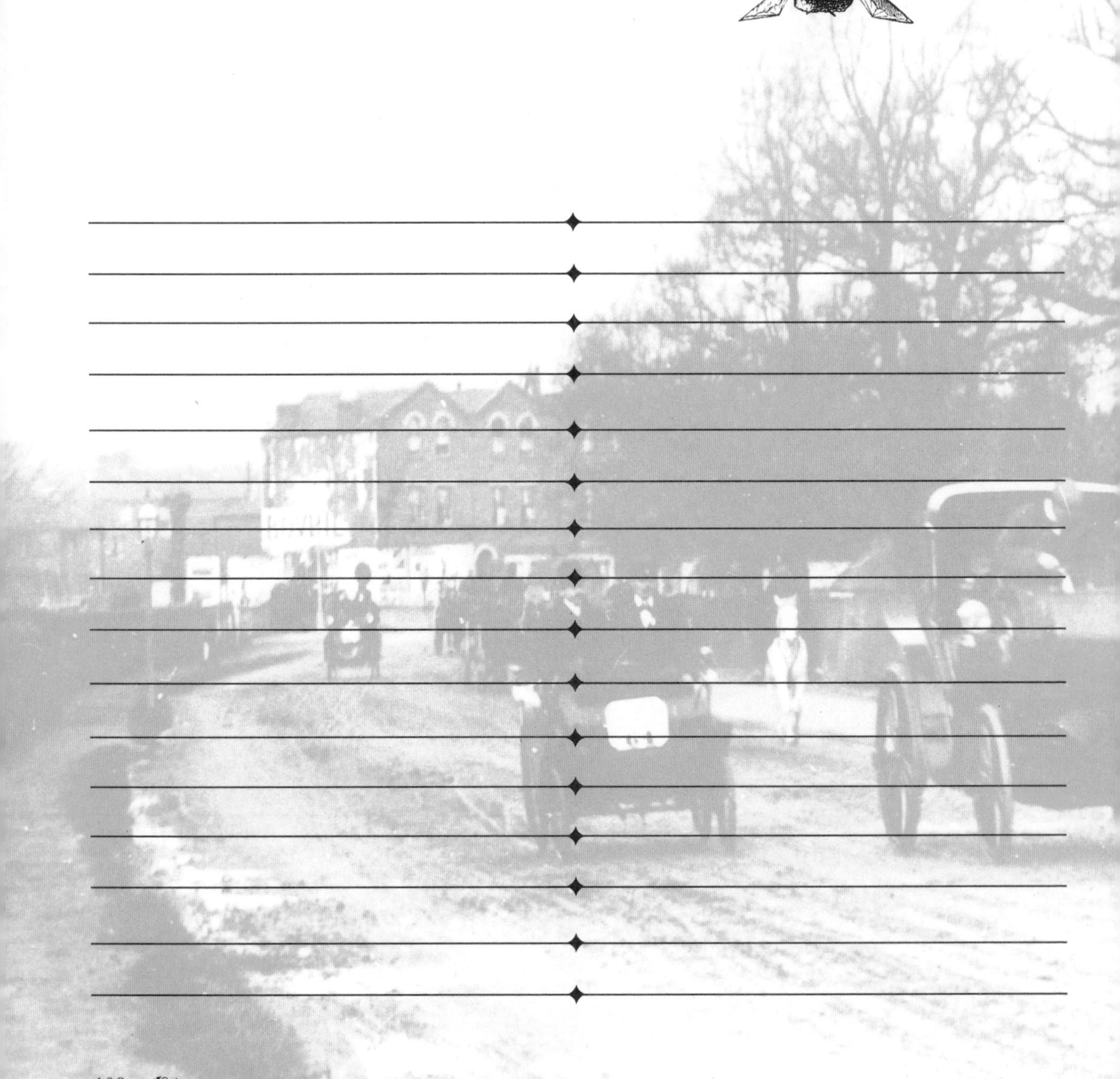

FAMILY BELONGINGS

Family Heirlooms

Does your family have any treasures? Sometimes valuable objects such as rings or furniture carry great sentimental value. Are there items that have been passed down from one generation to the next in your family?

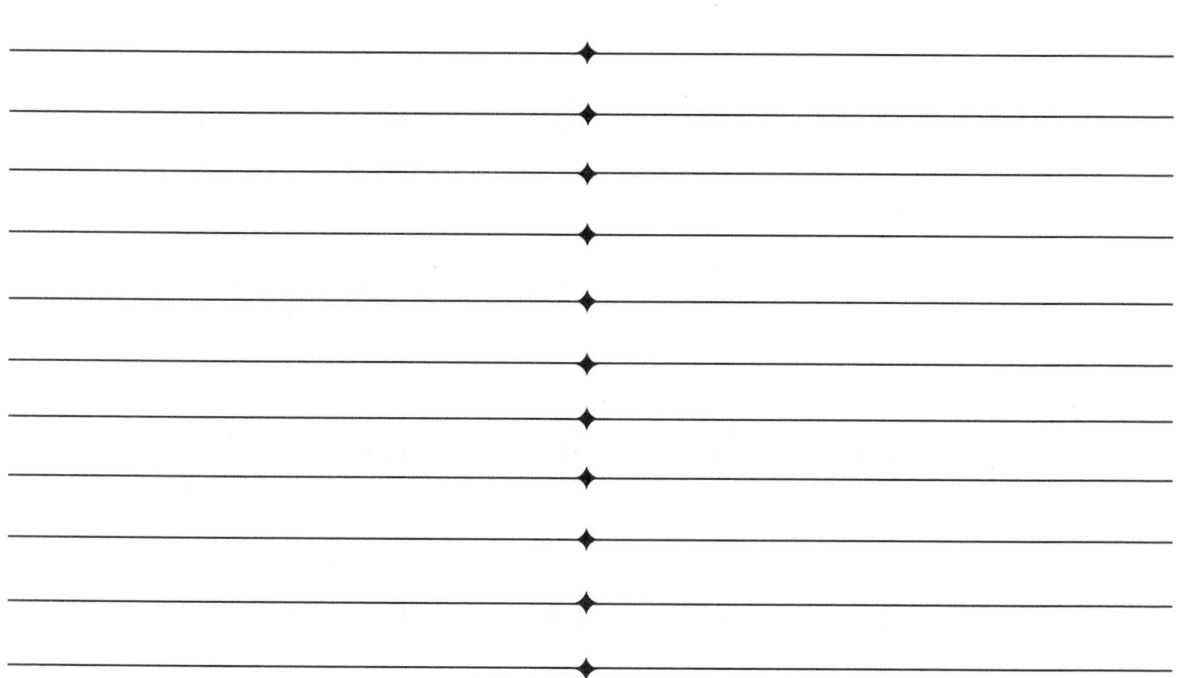

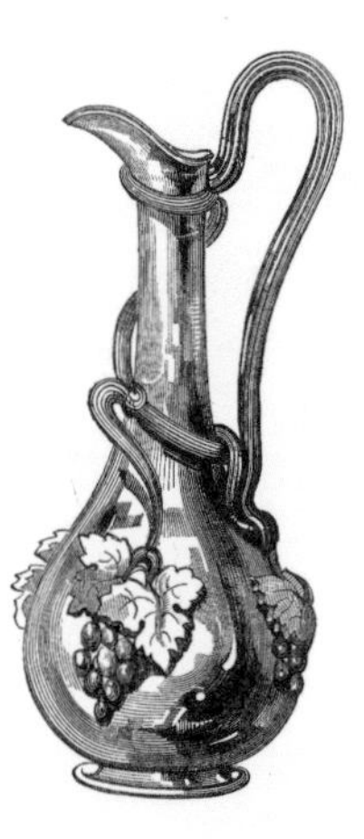

GALLERY OF MEMORIES

Select and place those special photographs of family, friends, pets, homes and events that have shaped your family's history here.

GALLERY OF MEMORIES

GALLERY OF MEMORIES

Select and place those special photographs of family, friends, pets, homes and events that have shaped your family's history here.

GALLERY OF MEMORIES

GALLERY OF MEMORIES

Select and place those special photographs of family, friends, pets, homes and events that have shaped your family's history here.

GALLERY OF MEMORIES

GALLERY OF MEMORIES

Select and place those special photographs of family, friends, pets, homes and events that have shaped your family's history here.

GALLERY OF MEMORIES

GALLERY OF MEMORIES

Select and place those special photographs of family, friends, pets, homes and events that have shaped your family's history here.